Molly

2014

Ready® Common Core

Reading **Instruction** 4

point of view
main idea
character

Curriculum Associates

Ready Common Core   Reading

Ready Common Core   Reading

Common Core   Reading

Curriculum Associates LLC

Common Core   Reading

Curriculum Associates

Acknowledgments

Elana Kopel, "Flying with a Tiger," from *Highlights,* January 2011. Copyright © 2011 by Highlights for Children, Inc., Columbus, OH. Reprinted with permission.

Lois Miner Huey, "Fulton's Success" from *Cobblestone* issue: American Invention, July/August 2009. Copyright © 2009 by Carus Publishing Company. Published by Cobblestone Publishing, 30 Grove Street, Suite C, Peterborough, NH 03458. Reprinted with permission. All rights reserved.

David Goodsell, "Sugar and Salt, Ice and Water: A Fun Experiment" from *Fun for Kidz,* January 2010. Copyright © 2010 by David Goodsell. Reprinted with permission.

Steven Dowshen, MD, "Minerals" adapted from *Kids' Health Online.* Copyright © 1995-2012 by The Nemours Foundation/KidsHealth®. Reprinted with permission.

Peter Roop, "It All Began with *Spacewar!*" from *Cobblestone* issue: The History of Computer, June 1984. Copyright © 1984 by Carus Publishing Company. Published by Cobblestone Publishing, 30 Grove Street, Suite C, Peterborough, NH 03458. Reprinted with permission. All rights reserved.

Leigh Anderson and David Chandler, "Why Salt? Valuable Little Cubes" from *Appleseeds* issue: Why Salt?, March 2007. Copyright © 2007 by Carus Publishing Company. Published by Cobblestone Publishing, 30 Grove Street, Suite C, Peterborough, NH 03458. Reprinted with permission. All rights reserved.

Kids Discover, "And Away We Go: Rockets" adapted from *Kids Discover,* March 2012, Volume 22, Issue 3. Copyright © 2012 by Kids Discover. Reprinted with permission.

Rachel Field, "Roads" from *Favorite Poems, Old and New: Selected Poems for Boys and Girls.*

Sam Walter Foss, "The House by the Side of the Road" from *Dreams in Homespun,* published by Lee & Shepard (1897).

Geoffrey Howard, "The Beach Road by the Woods" from *A Treasury of War Poetry: British and American Poems of the World War,* published by Houghton Mifflin (1917).

"The Two Frogs" from *The Violet Fairy Book,* edited by Andrew Lang, published by Longmans, Green & Company (1901).

E. Nesbit after William Shakespeare, "King Lear" from *Beautiful Stories from Shakespeare,* published by D. E. Cunningham & Co. (1907).

Maude L. Radford, "Sir Ivaine" from *King Arthur and His Knights,* published by Rand McNally & Company (1903).

Eleanor Estes, "Share and Share Alike" from The Moffats. Copyright © 1941 by Eleanor Estes. Copyright © renewed 1969 by Eleanor Estes. Reprinted by permission of Harcourt Children's Books, an imprint of Houghton Mifflin Harcourt Publishing Company. All rights reserved.

Gallimard Jeunesse, excerpt from *The History of Movie Making.* Copyright © 1995 by Gallimard Jeunesse, SA. Reprinted with permission of Scholastic, Inc.

Tenzing Norgay, excerpt from *Tiger of the Snows.*

"*Titanic* Sinks Four Hours After Hitting Iceberg; 866 Rescued By *Carpathia,* Probably 1,250 Perish; Ismay Safe, Mrs. Astor Maybe, Noted Names Missing" from *The New York Times,* April 16, 1912.

Sinking of the Titanic *and Great Sea Disasters,* edited by Logan Marshall, published by L. T. Myers (1912).

Sally Ride with Susan Okie excerpt from *To Space and Back.* Copyright © 1986 by Susan Okie and Sally Ride. Used by permission of HarperCollins.

John Noble Wilford, "Shuttle Rockets to Orbit with 5 Aboard" from *The New York Times,* June 19, 1983. Copyright © 1983 by The New York Times. All rights reserved. Used by permission and protected by the Copyright Laws of the United States. The printing, copying, redistribution, or retransmission of this Content without expressed, written permission is prohibited. http://www.thenewyorktimes.com/

Marcia Amidon Lusted, "Ferris's Grand Idea" from *Cobblestone* issue: A Fair to Remember, February 2009. Copyright © 2009 by Carus Publishing Company. Published by Cobblestone Publishing, 30 Grove Street, Suite C, Peterborough, NH 03458. Reprinted with permission. All rights reserved.

Denton J. Snider, "The Ferris Wheel" from *World's Fair Studies,* published by Sigma Publishing Company (1893).

Oliver Herford, "The Catfish" from *The Book of Humorous Verse,* compiled by Carolyn Wells, published by George H. Doran Company (1920).

E. A. Guest, "Can't" from *A Heap O' Livin',* published by Reilly & Lee Co. (1916).

W. M. Thackeray, "A Tragic Story" from *The Book of Humorous Verse,* compiled by Carolyn Wells, published by George H. Doran Company (1920).

D. L. Ashliman, "The Sound of Money." Copyright © 2012 by D. L. Ashliman. Reprinted with permission.

Janet Bitikofer, "Mapping Maps: Robots on the Red Planet" from *Appleseeds* issue: Maps and Mappers, November 2005. Copyright © 2005 by Carus Publishing Company. Published by Cobblestone Publishing, 30 Grove Street, Suite C, Peterborough, NH 03458. Reprinted with permission. All rights reserved.

Edward Richard Shaw, "Henry Hudson" from *Explorers and Discoverers,* published by American Book Publishers (1900).

John Bach McMaster, "The Coming of the Dutch" from *A Brief History of the United States,* published by American Book Company (1907).

"Air Works for Me" from *The Courage to Soar* by National Aeronautics and Space Administration, Marshall Space Flight Center Exploration Systems Mission Directorate: Ares Projects. Courtesy of NASA.

Count Lev. N. Tolstoy, "The Peasant and the Cucumbers" from *Fables for Children,* trans. and ed. by Leo Wiener, published by J. M. Dent and Company (1904).

D. L. Ashliman, "The Two-headed Weaver." Copyright © 2012 by D. L. Ashliman. Reprinted with permission.

Charles Perrault , "The Ridiculous Wishes" from *Old-Time Stories Told by Master Charles Perrault,* translated by A. E. Johnson, published by Dodd Mead and Company (1921).

F. Anton Schiefner, "The Monkeys and the Moon" from *Tibetan Tales Derived from Indian Sources,* translated by W. R. S. Ralston, published by Kegan Paul, Trench, Trubner, and Company (1906).

Mary Hoffman, "The King's Fire Dog" from *Sun, Moon, and Stars.* Copyright © 1998 by Mary Hoffman. Reproduced with permission of the author c/o Rogers, Coleridge & White Ltd., 20 Powis Mews, London W11 1JN.

"How Maui Snared the Sun" from *Hawaiian Folk Tales: A Collection of Native Legends,* compiled by Thos. G. Thrum, published A.C. McClurg & Company (1907).

Common Core State Standards © Copyright 2010. National Governors Association Center for Best Practices and Council of Chief State School Officers. All rights reserved.

Language Arts Florida Standards (LAFS) © 2104. Florida Department of Education.

Project Manager: Rob Hill
Cover Designer and Illustrator: Julia Bourque
Book Design: Mark Nodland

ISBN 978-0-7609-8555-7
©2014—Curriculum Associates, LLC
North Billerica, MA 01862

Table of Contents

Table of Contents

Table of Contents

Language Handbook

Table of Contents

Unit 1
Key Ideas and Details in Informational Text

How are readers like detectives? For starters, both readers and detectives are curious. Just as a detective asks questions and hunts for clues, a good reader looks for **key ideas** and **details** in a text. Being detective-like is important when reading history, science, technical and other informational texts. Sometimes, the answers to questions about key ideas and details will be as clear as footprints in the sand. They can lead a detective right to a solution. Other times, you'll need to read between the lines (or footprints!) to find an answer not directly stated in the text.

In this unit, you'll learn to recognize how one event leads to another and how one thing can cause another to happen. You'll also practice putting together what you read with what you know to come up with new ideas. With these reading skills, you'll be on your way to solving the mystery of the main idea: what a text is all about. So read like a detective. Pick up your magnifying glass—or, rather, your book—and start reading!

✓ Self Check

Before starting this unit, check off the skills you know below. As you complete each lesson, see how many more you can check off!

I know how to:	Before this unit	After this unit
find the main idea of an informational text.	☑	☐
explain how key details support the main idea of an informational text.	☑	☐
explain what happened and why based on information presented in historical, scientific, and technical texts.	☑	☐
summarize an informational text.	☑	☐
refer to details and examples when explaining and inferring what a text says.	☑	☐

Lesson 1   **Part 1: Introduction** 👥

Finding Main Ideas and Details

CCSS
RI.4.2: Determine the main idea of a text and explain how it is supported by key details. . . .

Theme: *People and Their Animals*

Has someone ever said to you, "Get to the point"? If so, what they mean is, "Tell me the main idea." In reading, the **main idea** is the most important idea in a text. **Key details** support the main idea by telling you more about it.

The main idea often appears early in a paragraph or passage. Key details that say more about the main idea usually follow right after.

Read the text below. Underline the main idea. Circle key details that support it.

Lewis and Clark's Faithful Companion

When Lewis and Clark explored the western United States, a dog named Seaman protected them. One night, a large buffalo came near their tent. Seaman chased the buffalo away. Another night, a grizzly bear entered their camp. Seaman barked and barked at the bear. He barked until the bear ran away. Seaman also protected Lewis and Clark by making sure they had food. Every day, Seaman hunted squirrels for the men to eat.

Read the diagram below. It identifies the text's main idea and key details. Complete the diagram by filling in a third key detail.

Main Idea
Seaman protected Lewis and Clark.

Key Detail	Key Detail	Key Detail
Seaman chased away a buffalo.	Seaman barked at a grizzly bear until it ran away.	Every day, Seaman hunted squirrels for the men to eat.

As you read, look for the main idea and the key details that support it. Remember, a diagram like the one shown above can help you keep track of both.

Read the first paragraph of a science passage about a snake and a snake charmer.

Genre: **Science**

The Snake and the Charmer   *by Sylvester Capello*

You have probably viewed the following scene in a movie or on TV. A snake charmer sits in front of a straw basket and plays a flute-like instrument. Suddenly, from inside the basket, a long, hooded cobra rises up. As the snake charmer plays the music, the cobra sways back and forth. The snake appears to be swaying in rhythm to the music. But, in fact, nothing could be further from the truth.

(continued)

Explore how to answer this question: *"What is the main idea of this paragraph?"*

To figure out the main idea of this paragraph, look for key details about the snake and the charmer. Then ask yourself what those key details tell you about the snake and the charmer.

The diagram below identifies three key details. Complete the first two details. What main idea do all of the details support? Tell about that idea on the lines following the diagram.

Main Idea
?

Key Detail	Key Detail	Key Detail
The snake charmer plays a *the snake charmer plays the music.*	As the charmer plays the flute, *the cobra sways back and forth.*	The music seems to be what makes the snake sway back and forth, but that is not true.

What is the main idea of the paragraph? Use details from the chart in your answer.

_____

_____

_____

_____

Continue reading the passage "The Snake and the Charmer." Use the Close Reading and the Hint to help you answer the question below.

Close Reading

What really makes the snake sway back and forth? **Underline** a sentence that tells why the snake sways.

(continued from page 4)

In reality, the cobra is quite deaf. It has no ears and can only sense vibrations in the ground. What the cobra sways to is not the music. It sways to the motion of the flute that the snake charmer moves back and forth as he plays. The cobra is trying to get into position to strike at the flute. However, as long as the snake charmer keeps the flute in motion, the snake cannot attack.

The Indian cobra is a favorite of snake charmers because daylight interferes with the snake's ability to strike. At night, however, the Indian cobra is extremely dangerous and more accurate. Cobras don't normally attack people, however. Instead, they go after frogs, fish, birds, and small mammals.

Hint

Which choice tells what the whole passage is about?

Circle the correct answer.

What is the main idea of "The Snake and the Charmer"?

A   The snake sways to the sound of the charmer's flute music.

B   Indian cobras have poor hearing, so they hunt best at night.

C   Snake charmers prefer the Indian cobra to other snakes.

D   The flute's motion, not its music, is what makes the snake sway.

✎ **Show Your Thinking**

Look at the answer you chose above. Explain how details in the text helped you figure out the main idea of "The Snake and the Charmer."

I know this because it says in the text it sways to the motion of the flute that the snake charmer moves back and forth as he plays.

Read the social studies passage. Use the Study Buddy and the Close Reading to guide your reading.

Genre: **Social Studies**

First, I'll try to figure out the main idea of what I read. Then I'll look for key details that support the main idea.

Close Reading

Paragraph 2 tells how hearing dogs alert their owners to sounds. **Circle** the names of these sounds.

Paragraphs 2 and 3 each tell how hearing dogs help people. In both paragraphs, **underline** a sentence that tells the main idea of that paragraph.

Lending an Ear   *by Michael Simon*

1   Mitzi, a Labrador retriever, is always by her owner Leah's side. This isn't just because Mitzi and Leah like each other. Mitzi is Leah's hearing dog. Leah is mostly deaf, and Mitzi's job is to alert Leah to sounds she cannot hear. Mitzi is happy as a constant, helpful companion for Leah.

2   Hearing dogs listen for sounds that people with hearing loss cannot hear. These dogs alert their owners to sounds by touching them with their nose or paw. After giving the alert, hearing dogs lead their owners to the source of the sound. Hearing dogs can be trained to recognize many household sounds. These sounds include doorbells, telephones, oven timers, alarm clocks, and fire and smoke alarms. Hearing dogs keep their deaf or partly deaf partners both active and safe by alerting them to such important noises.

3   Hearing dogs don't just help around the home. They also help their partners live and thrive in the world outside. People who can't hear sometimes feel lonely and isolated from other people. Hearing dogs can help their partners feel comfortable in public by making them aware of sounds. A hearing dog must wear an orange coat when in public. This tells other people that the dog's owner has some degree of hearing loss. Those other people can then adjust their own behavior when it is necessary.

4   Living and working side-by-side every day, hearing dogs and their partners become a special team—just like Mitzi and Leah.

Hints

Suppose a friend asks you what paragraph 1 is all about. Which is the best answer?

Use the Hints on this page to help you answer the questions.

1 What is the main idea expressed in paragraph 1?

   A Mitzi is always by her owner's side.

   B Mitzi is a hearing dog to Leah.

   C Mitzi and Leah like each other.

   D Leah, who is Mitzi's owner, is mostly deaf.

The correct choice is the one that the key detail most clearly supports.

2 Read this sentence from paragraph 2. It is a key detail.

> These sounds include doorbells, telephones, oven timers, alarm clocks, and fire and smoke alarms.

What idea in paragraph 2 does this key detail support?

   A Hearing dogs can be trained to recognize many sounds.

   B Hearing dogs use a nose or a paw to alert their owners to sounds.

   C Hearing dogs help their owners feel more comfortable in public.

   D Hearing dogs do many things to help people with hearing loss.

What is the passage about? What key details most clearly support its main idea?

3 Describe the main idea of "Lending an Ear." Then find at least two key details and tell how they support the main idea.

_____

_____

_____

_____

_____

_____

_____

Read the article. Then answer the questions that follow.

Flying with a Tiger

by Elana Kopel, Highlights

1   I am a zookeeper at the Dallas Zoo in Texas. One of my jobs is to care for Sumatran tigers.

2   These tigers live in the wild on the island of Sumatra and in some other parts of Asia. They are endangered, and their numbers are declining. But zoos around the world keep a few of the big cats to teach people about tigers and to let the tigers have cubs.

3   When a zoo wants a new tiger, it tries to get one from another zoo. That way, more tigers can stay in the wild. Some animals travel from zoo to zoo by truck, and some go by airplane. When we moved one of our tigers, a female named Skylar, to the San Francisco Zoo in California, she went by plane. I went along to help keep her safe.

Skylar in the Sky

4   Skylar spent the first two years of her life wrestling with her sister and stalking and pouncing on her brother. This is how tigers learn to hunt. By the age of three, Skylar was old enough to leave her siblings and start her own family. That's what she would have done in the wild.

5   Before Skylar could take to the skies, we needed to prepare her for the journey. We trained her to go into a shipping crate and let us close the door behind her. When she cooperated, we gave her an uncooked meatball, her favorite treat. . . .

Meatballs Galore

6   When moving day arrived, we put lots of meatballs inside Skylar's crate. Once Skylar was inside, the crate was loaded into the back of a truck. Skylar turned around in the crate to see what was happening, but she was quiet and calm the whole way to the airport.

7   Skylar and I flew on an airplane that carries packages, not people. Skylar's crate was loaded on with other large packages. . . . The plane left at midnight, and we stopped in Indiana to change aircraft. While we waited at the Indiana airport, I peeked into Skylar's crate. I was happy to see her sleeping peacefully.

8   Our second plane landed in San Francisco at eight o'clock in the morning. A zookeeper from the San Francisco Zoo met us and took us to Skylar's new home. . . . I knew Skylar was

nervous. She did not come out of the crate as quickly as she had gone in. She growled at her new zookeepers. We left her alone to calm down.

9   Skylar's new keepers took me to see the tiger exhibit where Skylar would be living. I told them that Skylar liked to take a dip in her swimming pool and to play with plastic barrels, giant plastic balls, empty plastic flowerpots, perfume-scented logs, and ice. . . . By the next day, Skylar had calmed down a little.

10   After my last visit with Skylar, I returned to Dallas on a regular airplane. I knew I would miss Skylar, but I hoped that she would like her new zoo and teach the people of San Francisco about the wildlife of Asia. I hoped she would start a new family, too.

More Tigers in the World

11   Months later, Skylar gave birth to three male cubs. She is a good mom, and she has brought more Sumatran tigers into the world. Maybe one day her cubs will be dads and there will be even more of these beautiful creatures.

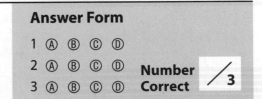

Answer Form

1 Ⓐ Ⓑ Ⓒ Ⓓ
2 Ⓐ Ⓑ Ⓒ Ⓓ   **Number**
3 Ⓐ Ⓑ Ⓒ Ⓓ   **Correct**   / 3

1   Which of these statements about Sumatran tigers does the passage **best** support?

   A   They are healthier when left out in the wild.

   B   They can help teach people to better respect wildlife.

   C   Many of them grow up in zoos before being set free.

   D   Many of them never learn how to hunt.

2   Why does the author describe Skylar's favorite treat?

   A   to explain how the zookeepers got Skylar into her crate

   B   to tell why Skylar enjoys living at the zoo

   C   to suggest that tigers like eating food made for people

   D   to compare what tigers eat in the wild to what they eat in zoos

3   Read this sentence from paragraph 3. It is a key detail.

    Some animals travel from zoo to zoo by truck, and some go by airplane.

What idea in paragraph 3 does this key detail support?

A   Zoos sometimes want more tigers.

B   Skylar was moved to the San Francisco Zoo.

C   Skylar needed to prepare for her journey.

D   Zoos try not to take tigers from the wild.

4   One central idea of the article is that Sumatran tigers need our help. Write a paragraph explaining the key points that support this idea. Use at least **two** details from the article to support your answer.

_____

_____

_____

_____

_____

_____

_____

_____

_____

_____

✓ **Self Check**   *Go back and see what you can check off on the Self Check on page 1.*

Lesson 2   Part 1: Introduction 👥

Understanding Historical Texts

CCSS

RI.4.3: Explain events [and] ideas . . . in a historical . . . text, including what happened and why, based on specific information in the text.

Theme: *Transportation History*

A **history text** tells you about events that happened in the past. Most history texts don't just describe the events that happened or the ideas people had. They also explain why those events happened and where those ideas came from.

Look at the photos below. One photo shows an event that happened. The other photo shows why it happened.

Photo of What Happened

Photo of Why It Happened

ROAD WORK AHEAD

In the table below, first describe the event that happened. Then explain why that event happened. Use details from the photos to support your answers.

Description of What Happened	Explanation for Why It Happened

If you are asked to describe what happened and then explain why, do the following:

- First, look for details in the text that answer this question: "What happened?"

- Then, look for details that answer this question: "Why did this happen?"

Describing and explaining historical events is a powerful skill. It's useful not just for reading about history but also for understanding what happens around you every day.

Read the first paragraph of a history passage about a famous car called the "Model T."

Genre: **History**

The Model T   *by Thomas A. Moore*

When the first cars were produced, only wealthy people could afford them. Henry Ford wanted to build a car that the average working person could afford. In 1908, the Ford Motor Company introduced a new, low-cost car. It was called the Model T and sold for $825. Although the car was reasonably priced, Ford kept thinking of ways to make it even cheaper. He knew that the lower the price, the more customers he would gain and the more money he would make.

(continued)

Explore how to answer this question: *"What event happened in 1908, and why did it happen? Use details from the text in your answer."*

Look at the table below. It will help you describe what happened in 1908. It will then help you explain why that event happened.

Description of What Happened	Explanation for Why It Happened
In 1908, the Ford Motor Company introduced _____ _____ . The car sold for _____ .	Henry Ford did this because he wanted to build _____ _____ _____ .

Now, using details from the table, answer these questions in your own words.

What event happened in 1908? _____

_____

_____

Why did this event happen? _____

_____

_____

Continue reading the passage "The Model T." Use the Close Reading and the Hint to answer the question below.

Close Reading

Underline a sentence that tells an event that happened in 1913. Then **draw a box** around a sentence that tells why that event happened.

(continued from page 12)

Ford's early cars were all handcrafted. This meant that each automobile was slightly different from the next. It also meant that each took a long time to make. Ford decided his cars would no longer be handcrafted. They would be put together in exactly the same way, saving time and money. In 1913, Ford began producing cars with the help of a moving assembly line.

The moving assembly line achieved Ford's goal of turning out a car faster and for increasingly lower prices. In time, Ford's factory was turning out one automobile every 90 minutes. By 1915, the Ford Motor Company was earning record profits. And by 1918, half of all cars in the United States were Model Ts. Almost overnight, the United States became a nation on wheels.

Hint

Which choice tells how the moving assembly line changed the making of cars?

Circle the correct answer.

Which of the following sentences explains why Henry Ford began using a moving assembly line to make cars?

A   He knew that it would make bigger cars.

B   He noticed the small differences between handcrafted cars.

C   He wanted to make cars more quickly and cheaply than before.

D   He hoped that by 1918 nearly half of all cars would be Model Ts.

✎ Show Your Thinking

Before 1913, the Model Ts were all slightly different from each other. Look back into the text to find why this was so. On the lines below, explain why they were slightly different.

_____

_____

_____

Read the history passage. Use the Study Buddy and the Close Reading to guide your reading.

History texts tell what happened in the past and why it happened. As I read, I'll look for both descriptions and explanations.

Close Reading

What happened when foot pedals were added? In the first paragraph, **underline** a sentence that tells what happened.

What could happen to the rider of a high-wheel bicycle? **Circle** a detail that tells what could happen.

Genre: **History**

The Bicycle's First Century   *by J. Soo*

1   Two centuries ago, bicycles did not look like the bikes you know today. Invented by a Frenchman around 1790, the first bicycle had two wheels and a wooden frame. It worked like a scooter. In 1816, a German improved on this design. He connected a bar to the front wheel. This allowed the rider to steer the bicycle. Then, in 1839, a Scottish blacksmith made yet another improvement. He added foot pedals, which let riders put force on the wheels.

2   In the 1870s, the "high-wheel" bicycle appeared. It was called this because the front wheel was far larger than the rear wheel. The pedals turned the front wheel only, but the size of that wheel meant that each turn of the pedals took the rider a great distance. On the high-wheel bicycle, the rider sat up high, near the front axle. Consequently, when the large front wheel struck a rut or rock in the road, the rider could be pitched head-first over the front of the bicycle! The high-wheel bicycle wasn't very safe.

3   In 1885, an Englishman made the first "safety" bicycle. The bicycle was now beginning to look more like the modern one you see every day. Its front and rear wheels were the same size, and sprockets and chains linked the two wheels together. In the 1890s, inventors added air-filled rubber tires. Then came a coaster brake and adjustable handlebars. The first hundred years of the bicycle—from 1790 to the 1890s—brought many changes, and the next century would bring even more improvements.

Hints

Putting the bar on the front wheel let riders do something new. What was it?

How was the bicycle improved in 1839? What effect did it have?

First, tell what the danger was. Then tell what feature of the bike helped make the danger happen.

Use the Hints on this page to help you answer the questions.

1 Read the following sentences from paragraph 1.

> In 1816, a German improved on this design. He connected a bar to the front wheel.

What happened as a result of the German's improvement?

  A   The bicycle began to work like a scooter.

  B   The rider was able to steer the bicycle.

  C   The rider could put force on the wheels.

  D   The bicycle did not look like the bikes of today.

2 Which sentence best explains what happened in 1839 and why?

  A   An inventor put two wheels of the same size on a bicycle, which resulted in the first safety bicycle.

  B   A bicycle called the "high-wheel" was given this name because of its large front wheel.

  C   The addition of foot pedals in 1839 gave the bicycle a more modern look.

  D   Riders were able to apply force to the bicycle's wheels because an inventor had added foot pedals.

3 Describe what could happen to the rider of a high-wheel bicycle. Then explain how the bicycle helped cause this problem. Support your answer with at least two details from the passage.

_____

_____

_____

_____

_____

_____

_____

Read the history article below. Then answer the questions that follow.

from "Fulton's Success"

by Lois Miner Huey, Cobblestone

1   "Fulton's Folly," people jeered as they passed Browne's Shipyard in New York City. It was 1807, and Browne's was the site where inventor Robert Fulton and his partner, Robert R. Livingston, Jr., were building a very strange boat. The two men knew that putting a steam engine onboard a vessel was still new and dangerous. But they ignored the taunts. They were convinced that Fulton's steamboat ideas, combined with Livingston's financial backing, would revolutionize transportation in America. And they were right . . . .

2   On August 17, after devoting about five months to its construction, Fulton launched a vessel that measured 150 feet long, 13 feet wide, and 9 feet deep.

3   Fulton and a group of invited guests prepared to steam up the Hudson River from New York City to Albany, the state capital. The guests had to put up with primitive

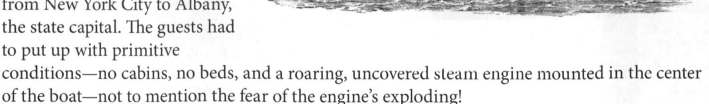

conditions—no cabins, no beds, and a roaring, uncovered steam engine mounted in the center of the boat—not to mention the fear of the engine's exploding!

4   They cast off at 1 P.M. The vessel puffed away from the dock—and stalled. The passengers' whispering turned into loud mumbles, which eventually gave way to shouts of dismay. Sensing their fear, Fulton promised to return to the dock if he could not fix the problem.

5   After a short time, there was a huge blast of smoke. Once again, the boat churned upriver. Described as looking like a giant teakettle, the vessel's engine let off steam, raining down sparks that sizzled in the water. The noise was deafening, but the boat was moving, and the passengers cheered. Chugging upstream against the tide at a fast four to five miles per hour, it easily passed sailing ships and fishing craft.

6   In its wake, the boat's two side paddlewheels left waves of foamy water—and lots of terrified onlookers. Nothing like it ever had been seen before. Darkness fell, but the boat continued its journey. With a full moon and warm breezes, the passengers stayed up all night singing songs by candlelight. They had mostly forgotten their fears.

7   The next day, the boat docked at Livingston's estate, called Clermont. After spending the night, it continued steaming to Albany the following morning. It pulled into that city at 5 P.M. on August 19, having made the 150-mile trip in 32 hours of travel time. Crowds cheered its arrival. No longer a joke, "Fulton's Folly" had become the first successful steamboat in America. . . .

Answer Form

1 Ⓐ Ⓑ Ⓒ Ⓓ
2 Ⓐ Ⓑ Ⓒ Ⓓ   **Number**
3 Ⓐ Ⓑ Ⓒ Ⓓ   **Correct** /3

1 What new idea did Robert Fulton have that would make him famous?

A spending five months building a boat in a shipyard

B taking passengers from New York City to Albany by boat

C using a steam engine to power a paddlewheel boat

D getting money from Robert Livingston to build the boat

2 The table below tells about an event that happened, according to the passage.

What Happened (the Effect)	Why It Happened (the Cause)
People called the boat "Fulton's Folly."	?

Which of the following should replace the "?" in the table?

A Fulton and Livingston were building a boat people thought was odd.

B On its first trip, the steamboat stalled right after it launched.

C Passengers were afraid the boat's steam engine would explode.

D After the boat stalled, it let off a huge blast of smoke.

3 Which sentence from the passage tells why Fulton and Livingston kept working on their boat even though others thought they were being foolish?

   A "The two men knew that putting a steam engine onboard a vessel was still new and dangerous."

   B "They were convinced that Fulton's steamboat ideas, combined with Livingston's financial backing, would revolutionize transportation in America."

   C "Fulton and a group of invited guests prepared to steam up the Hudson River from New York City to Albany, the state capital."

   D "It pulled into that city at 5 P.M. on August 19, having made the 150-mile trip in 32 hours of travel time."

4 Paragraph 7 states that Fulton's boat arrived in Albany. Describe how the crowd reacted to the vessel's arrival. Then explain why the crowd reacted that way. Use at least **one** detail from the passage to support both parts of your answer.

Description of how the crowd reacted to the vessel's arrival:

_____

_____

_____

Explanation of why the crowd reacted that way:

_____

_____

_____

_____

 ✓ **Self Check** *Go back and see what you can check off on the Self Check on page 1.*

Lesson 3   Part 1: Introduction 👥

Understanding Technical Texts

CCSS

RI.4.3: Explain . . . procedures, ideas, or concepts . . . in a . . . technical text, including what happened and why, based on specific information in the text.

Theme: *Making and Doing*

At some point, you've probably followed directions for putting together a toy or making food. If so, you were using **technical texts**, or texts that help you do a task.

Below is a recipe. Steps A through E are out of order. Under the column "What Step?," write which step should be first, which should be second, and so on. One step has been written in for you.

How to Make Smashamole

What You Need	What You Do	What Step?
• 2 avocados • 8 cherry tomatoes • 1 tablespoon onion powder • 1 tablespoon lime juice • 2 plastic zipper-seal bags • 1 unopened can of food	**A.** Roll the can over the bags to smash the food.	
	B. Put the first bag in the second bag. Zip the second bag.	
	C. When everything is smashed, open the bags. Put the Smashamole in a bowl. Use as a dip for chips.	
	D. Peel the avocados and remove the pits. Wash the cherry tomatoes and remove the stems.	
	E. Put the first four ingredients on the list into a bag. Zip the bag. Remove as much air as you can.	**Second**

Now put steps A through E in the correct order. One box has been done for you.

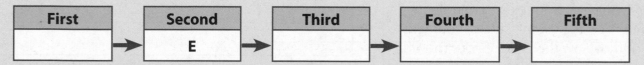

First	Second	Third	Fourth	Fifth
	E			

Some technical texts tell you why to follow certain steps. Other times, you have to figure it out. In the Smashamole recipe, why should you roll the can over the bags? If you don't, the ingredients won't be smashed, and you won't have Smashamole.

As you read a technical text, keep in mind not just what it tells you to do but also why it is telling you that. That way, you're not just following instructions—you're also learning something new.

Read the first part of a technical passage on finding your pulse rate.

Genre: **Technical**

Finding Your Pulse Rate *by Maria Arroyo*

Everyone has a pulse. As the heart pumps blood through our bodies, the pumping makes a rhythm you can measure. This rhythm is your pulse.

The **pulse rate** is a measure of the number of times the heart beats each minute. There are many reasons to find and check your pulse rate. Your pulse rate can tell a doctor how well your heart is working. It can also give important information about your overall health and fitness.

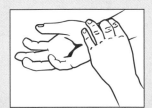

Follow these steps to find your pulse rate. First, place your index and middle fingers on the thumb side of your wrist, slightly below the base of your thumb. Then press gently until you feel the beat of your pulse.

(continued)

Explore how to answer these questions: *"What are the first two steps in finding your pulse rate? And, why is it a good idea to find and check your pulse rate?"*

First, look for the part of the text that gives steps for finding your pulse rate. Write a "1" by the first step and a "2" by the second step. Then complete the diagram below by filling out Step 2.

Step 1	Step 2
First, place your index and middle fingers on the thumb side of your wrist, slightly below the base of your thumb.	

The second paragraph gives two reasons for finding and checking your pulse rate. Find those reasons, **underline** both of them, and then write them in your own words on the lines below.

_____

_____

_____

Continue reading the passage about finding your pulse rate. Use the Close Reading and the Hint to help you answer the question.

Close Reading

To help keep the steps clear, **circle** words that show order of events, such as *next*, *then*, and *after*.

(continued from page 20)

After you find your pulse, use a watch to count the number of beats that occurs in 15 seconds. Then multiply this number by 4 to find the number of beats that occurs in one minute. Next, write the number on a piece of paper. The result is your pulse rate. If you were not exercising just before taking your pulse, then this is your **resting pulse rate**.

To find your **exercising pulse rate**, first run in place for 60 seconds or do 10 jumping jacks. After that, check your pulse rate and record it on a piece of paper. What is the difference between your resting and exercising rates? If they are different, what do you think is the cause of this difference?

Hint

Which sentence tells readers how to increase their pulse rates?

Circle the correct answer.

Which sentence tells what to do just before you measure your exercising pulse rate?

A "Use a watch to count the number of beats in 15 seconds."

B "Run in place for 60 seconds or do 10 jumping jacks."

C "Multiply the number of beats by 4 to find the overall pulse rate."

D "Find the difference between your resting and exercising rates."

✎ Show Your Thinking

What is your pulse? What causes it? Use details from the entire passage in your answer.

_____

_____

_____

Read the technical passage. Use the Study Buddy and the Close Reading to guide your reading.

This is a "how-to" text! I will picture in my mind what the text tells me to do. This will help me understand each step.

Close Reading

Part 2 tells you not to use too much paste. But why? **Underline** a sentence that tells why.

What is the purpose of the balloon? In Parts 1, 2, and 3, **circle** the word *balloon*. This will help you understand its purpose.

Genre: **Technical**

Making a Rhino Bank   *by Matt Kincaid*

Lots of people have piggy banks. Here's how to make something different—a rhino bank. You will need:

- a round balloon
- newspaper torn into strips
- a large bowl of papier-mâché (PAY per meh SHAY) paste
- cardboard tubes from paper towels or toilet paper
- masking tape

Part 1: Blow up the balloon and tie a knot. Cut the cardboard tube into four short lengths and tape them to the balloon as "legs." Roll some newspaper into the shape of a cone and tape it to the front of the balloon, as a horn. Make sure the form looks like a rhino (not a pig). This is, after all, a rhino bank.

Part 2: Dip one strip of newspaper into the papier-mâché paste. Use your fingers to squeeze extra paste back into the bowl. Then stick the pasted strip over the balloon and smooth it down. Continue dipping and placing strips, one at a time, until you have completely covered your creation. Do not use any more paste than is necessary. If there is too much paste, the strips will not lay flat and might not stick to each other.

Part 3: After 24 hours, the paste will be dry and the shape will harden. Have an adult cut a coin slot in the top with a knife. The balloon will pop. You can paint and decorate your rhino bank if you want. A rhino bank is much better than a piggy bank!

Hints

You need to identify the purpose of Part 1, not just a detail from it.

Use the Hints on this page to help you answer the questions.

1 In "Making a Rhino Bank," which of the following best describes the purpose of the section titled "Part 1"?

A It tells how to blow up the balloon and tie a knot.

B It explains how to make the rhino form.

C It shows how a rhino looks different than a pig.

D It lists the materials needed to make the rhino bank.

Look for details that tell what happens if you use too much paste.

2 The sentences below are from Part 2 of "Making a Rhino Bank."

Dip one strip of newspaper into the papier-mâché paste. Use your fingers to squeeze extra paste back into the bowl.

Why should you squeeze extra paste back into the bowl?

A You need to dip newspaper strips into the bowl of papier-mâché paste.

B If you run out of paste, it will take you much longer to complete your rhino bank.

C You must remove the extra paste before putting the strip on the balloon.

D Too much paste on the newspaper strips might make it difficult to finish the rhino bank.

Is the balloon less important by Part 3 than it was in Part 1? If so, why?

3 Explain why popping the balloon in Part 3 will not destroy the rhino bank. Use at least two details from the text to support your response.

_____

_____

_____

_____

_____

_____

Read the following science experiment. Then answer the questions that follow.

Sugar and Salt, Ice and Water: A Fun Experiment

by David Goodsell, Fun for Kidz

If you live near a lake or pond in a cold climate, the lake or pond might freeze if the temperature gets cold enough. But if you live near an ocean or a bay, even though it gets just as cold, the water does not freeze as easily. Why? What would happen if the oceans were made up of sugar water instead of salt water? Yummm!

No matter where you live, you can perform this easy and fun experiment to compare how fast regular water, sugar water, and salt water freeze. You'll be using the freezing compartment of your refrigerator. You will need:

- three clear plastic cups
- clear tape and paper for labels
- sugar
- salt
- measuring cups and spoons

You'll also need an experiment chart on a large piece of notebook paper like the one shown on the next page.

1   Put paper labels on each cup. Write SALT on one. Write SUGAR on one. Write REG (which stands for REGULAR) on the third.

2   Pour 3/4 cup of tap water into each of the three cups.

3   Add 1 tablespoon of salt to the SALT cup. Stir the water until the salt is dissolved.

4   Add 1 tablespoon of sugar to the SUGAR cup. Stir until the sugar is dissolved.

5   Place the three cups on the same shelf in your freezer.

6   Check the cups every half hour, starting after one hour. In addition to looking at them, put a finger into each cup. Wash your finger off before putting it into the next cup. You don't want salt in your sugar water!

7   On the chart write your observations.

Time (hours)	Regular Water	Sugar Water	Salt Water
1			
1.5			
2			
2.5			
3			
3.5			
4			
4.5			

You will find that the regular water will freeze first. The sugar water will gradually freeze, becoming "slushy," like those "icy" drinks you get at the convenience store, before freezing like a freezer pop. It will take much longer for the salt water to freeze.

What Happens?

When the sugar and salt crystals dissolve in the water, they break down into hundreds of thousands of tiny particles you can't even see. This lowers the temperature at which the water will freeze. The more particles there are, the lower will be the freezing temperature. There happens to be far more salt particles in a tablespoon of salt than sugar particles in a tablespoon of sugar. So, you will discover that salt water will freeze at a lower temperature than sugar water.

1 Why is it important to label the cups at the beginning of the experiment?

Answer Form

1 Ⓐ Ⓑ Ⓒ Ⓓ **Number**

2 Ⓐ Ⓑ Ⓒ Ⓓ **Correct** /2

A You will be placing all of the cups into the freezer later in the experiment.

B The cup of salt water will freeze more slowly than the cup of sugar water.

C The cup of regular water looks different than the other two cups.

D You must know the type of water in each cup to understand the results.

2 In the passage, Step 6 says, "Wash your finger off before putting it into the next cup. You don't want salt in your sugar water!"

Why should you wash off your finger before sticking it into the next cup?

A A mixture of salt water and sugar water will freeze more quickly than pure sugar water will.

B If you mix salt water with sugar water, you won't know whether the salt or the sugar is affecting the water's freezing point.

C A mixture of salt water and sugar water will cause the salt and sugar crystals to dissolve into the water.

D Mixing salt and sugar in water will produce a blend of ice and slush.

3 The experiment compared the time needed to freeze identical amounts of regular water, sugar water, and salt water.

List the order in which the three types of water froze, from quickest to slowest.

_____

The first paragraph asks, "What would happen if the oceans were made up of sugar water instead of salt water?" Answer this question now. Use the words "temperature" and "freeze" in your answer.

_____

_____

_____

_____

_____

 **Self Check** *Go back and see what you can check off on the Self Check on page 1.*

Understanding Scientific Texts

CCSS
RI.4.3: Explain events, . . . ideas, or concepts . . . in a . . . scientific text, including what happened and why, based on specific information in the text.

Theme: *Minerals that Matter*

A good **scientific text** is like walking through a park with a nature guide at your side. Just like the guide, the text will tell you not just what is happening but also explain how and why it is happening.

Look at the cartoon below. It shows a natural process and tells how it happened.

In the table below, use what you see in the cartoon to describe what happened. Then, read the explanation of how it happened.

Description of What Happened	Explanation for How It Happened
_____ _____ _____ _____	Over a long time, the mud hardens and becomes rock. This keeps the buried skeleton safe. Much later, the ocean drains. With the ocean gone, erosion wears away the rock. After a long time, all of the rock is eroded away, revealing the skeleton.

When you are asked to explain how or why something happened, follow these steps:

- First, look for details that answer the question: "What happened?"

- Then, look for details that answer the question: "How or why did it happen?"

Most people ask questions such as "What happened?" and "How did it happen?" and "Why did it happen?" in their everyday lives. You can ask these questions not just of the world you live in but also of the texts you read—including scientific texts.

Read the first two paragraphs of a science passage about coal.

Genre: **Science**

Black Rock   *by Patrick Pierce*

Coal is an important source of energy in our country. It is made from plant matter that was buried far below the Earth's surface for millions of years. Being buried so deeply and for so long put the plant matter under intense heat and pressure. The heat and pressure caused the chemical and physical characteristics of the plant matter to change. Eventually, the plant matter turned into coal.

In addition to being a source of energy, a coal mine can give scientists an important view of the past. For example: Recently in Danville, Illinois, scientists found inside of a coal deposit some well-preserved images of trees, branches, and fallen leaves. These images were made by the trees, branches, and leaves of a forest that thrived millions upon millions of years ago.

(continued)

Explore how to answer these questions: *"What is coal made from? How is coal made? Use details from the text in your answers."*

- The question "What is coal made from?" asks you to tell what kind of matter turns into coal. Reread the text and **circle** examples of the kind of matter that turns into coal.

- The question "How is coal made?" asks you to explain how that kind of matter turns into coal. Reread the text and **underline** any text that tells how that matter turns into coal.

Now answer the questions, using complete sentences. Use details that you circled and underlined in your answers.

What is coal made from? _____

_____

How is coal made? _____

_____

_____

_____

Continue reading the science passage about coal. Use the Close Reading and the Hint to help you answer the question.

Close Reading

What sentence tells what happens when coal is mined and used as fuel? **Underline** that sentence.

(continued from page 28)

Today, generators fueled by coal supply much of the world's energy. But the processes we use to mine coal and convert it into fuel can pollute our air, land, and water. This leads to a conflict. We need to use coal, but we also need to protect our environment.

To solve this conflict, engineers have started developing new technologies to reduce potential air pollution. One new process is particularly promising. Coal and a rock called *limestone* are burned together in a mixture of sand and air. This process reduces the amount of pollution emitted from the burning coal.

Hint

Think about why it is important to reduce pollution.

Circle the correct answer.

Why are engineers developing new technologies related to reducing the pollution from coal?

A People rely on coal for a large percent of their energy needs.

B Mining coal and using it for fuel can damage the environment.

C They have made a process that uses coal to reduce pollution.

D Limestone will eventually replace coal as a source of energy.

✎ Show Your Thinking

Look at the answer you chose above. Explain why you think that choice was better than any of the other answers to the question. Use details from the passage in your explanation.

_____

_____

_____

Read the science passage. Use the Study Buddy and the Close Reading to guide your reading.

In science texts, explanations often appear near words such as "because," "therefore," and "reasons." I'll watch for these words as I read.

Close Reading

Paragraph 3 says that gold is often mixed with other metals. **Underline** details telling why that is.

Paragraph 4 tells about how gold is used today. **Circle** those details.

Genre: **Science**

Gold   *by Carl Gelb*

1   People have valued gold for thousands of years. Because of the metal's durability, gold ornaments, statues, and jewelry look as brilliant today as when the artists of ancient Egypt and other cultures crafted them thousands of years ago. Gold is one of nature's true wonders.

2   **Properties:** Gold is an element. It cannot be broken down into simpler substances. Gold is also very malleable, which means it is easily flattened into a thin sheet. Gold is also ductile, which means it can be pulled into a wire. For these reasons, gold is useful in making jewelry. One ounce of gold can become 187 square feet of gold leaf or one mile of gold wire. Gold also conducts heat and electricity very well.

3   **Alloys:** Pure gold is very soft. Because it's so soft, gold is often mixed with other metals to make a mixture, or alloy, that is stronger than gold alone. Adding silver, copper, and zinc to gold produces the color we associate with jewelry.

4   **Today's Uses:** In the past, gold was mainly used for jewelry, statues, and other decorations. But today we use gold for more than just its beauty. It is an excellent conductor of electricity. This means that electricity flows through it easily. As a conductor, gold coats electrical parts inside our cell phones and computers. It helps speed the flow of electricity. Thin films of gold also reflect radiation on satellites, the sun visors of space suits, and the windows of skyscrapers. Gold's uses are many and important!

Hints

A jewelry maker must shape, bend, and stretch metal.

Use the Hints below to help you answer the questions.

1 In paragraph 2, which detail tells you why gold is useful in making jewelry?

- **A** It conducts heat and electricity well.
- **B** It needs to be mixed with other metals.
- **C** It cannot be broken into simpler substances.
- **D** It is malleable and ductile.

What details in the text tell you how gold changes when mixed with other metals?

2 Which sentence best explains why gold is mixed with other metals?

- **A** Gold is an element, so it can be broken down into simpler parts and used to make wire.
- **B** Gold is soft, so it is combined with other metals to make a mixture that is stronger than gold alone.
- **C** Gold is a very soft metal, so it must be mixed with white gold to produce the yellow gold used in jewelry.
- **D** Gold is a good conductor, so it is often mixed with other metals to coat electrical parts inside cell phones.

Look for the properties of gold that make it useful in specific modern technologies.

3 Identify two modern technologies that use gold. Explain why people use gold in those technologies. Use at least two details from the passage to support your answer.

_____

_____

_____

_____

_____

_____

_____

_____

Read the science article. Then answer the questions that follow.

Minerals

by Steven Dowshen, MD, Kids' Health online

1   Did you ever notice how TV commercials for breakfast cereal always mention vitamins and minerals? But when you think of minerals, food isn't the first thing that comes to mind. Aren't minerals something you find in the earth, like iron and quartz?

2   Well, yes, but small amounts of some minerals are also in foods—for instance, red meat, such as beef, is a good source of iron.

3   Just like vitamins, minerals help your body grow, develop, and stay healthy. The body uses minerals to perform many different functions—from building strong bones to transmitting nerve impulses. Some minerals are even used to make hormones or maintain a normal heartbeat.

Macro and Trace

4   The two kinds of minerals are: macrominerals and trace minerals. *Macro* means "large" in Greek (and your body needs larger amounts of macrominerals than trace minerals). The macromineral group is made up of calcium, phosphorus, magnesium, sodium, potassium, chloride, and sulfur.

5   A *trace* of something means that there is only a little of it. So even though your body needs trace minerals, it needs just a tiny bit of each one. Scientists aren't even sure how much of these minerals you need each day. Trace minerals include iron, manganese, copper, iodine, zinc, cobalt, fluoride, and selenium.

6   Let's take a closer look at some of the minerals you get from food.

Calcium

7   Calcium is the top macromineral when it comes to your bones. This mineral helps build strong bones so you can do everything from standing up straight to scoring that winning goal. It also helps build strong, healthy teeth for chomping on tasty food.

Iron

8   The body needs iron to transport oxygen from your lungs to the rest of your body. Your entire body needs oxygen to stay healthy and alive. Iron helps because it's important in the formation of hemoglobin (say: hee-muh-glo-bun), which is the part of your red blood cells that carries oxygen throughout the body.

Potassium

9   Potassium (say: puh-tah-see-um) keeps your muscles and nervous system working properly. Did you know your blood and body tissues, such as muscles, contain water? They do, and potassium helps make sure the amount of water is just right.

Zinc

10   Zinc helps your immune system, which is your body's system for fighting off illnesses and infections. It also helps with cell growth and helps heal wounds, such as cuts.

WHAT FOODS CONTAIN THESE MINERALS?			
Calcium	**Iron**	**Potassium**	**Zinc**
milk	beef	bananas	beef
cheese	tuna	broccoli	pork
yogurt	eggs	tomatoes	lamb
broccoli	beans	potatoes	legumes

11   When people don't get enough of these important minerals, they can have health problems. For instance, too little calcium—especially when you're a kid—can lead to weaker bones. Some kids may take mineral supplements, but most kids don't need them if they eat a nutritious diet. So eat foods with those minerals and stay healthy!

Answer Form

1 Ⓐ Ⓑ Ⓒ Ⓓ
2 Ⓐ Ⓑ Ⓒ Ⓓ   **Number**   /3
3 Ⓐ Ⓑ Ⓒ Ⓓ   **Correct**

1   What could people interested in improving their diets learn from this article?

   A   how much of each trace mineral a body needs to be healthy

   B   what can happen if there is too much iron in a person's body

   C   which foods contain calcium, iron, potassium, and zinc

   D   why the body needs more macrominerals than trace minerals

2   Why does the human body need iron?

   A   to form the parts of blood cells that carry oxygen through the body

   B   to make sure the amount of water in body tissues is just right

   C   to help build strong bones and healthy teeth

   D   to keep the body's immune system working correctly

3   Which sentence from the passage tells what happens when the human body doesn't get enough calcium?

   A   "Calcium is the top macromineral when it comes to your bones."

   B   "It also helps with cell growth and helps heal wounds, such as cuts."

   C   "When people don't get enough of these important minerals, they can have health problems."

   D   "For instance, too little calcium—especially when you're a kid—can lead to weaker bones."

4   The human body needs iron, potassium, and zinc. Explain what can happen when a person doesn't get enough of these minerals. Use at least **three** details from the passage in your answer.

_____

_____

_____

_____

_____

 **Self Check**   *Go back and see what you can check off on the Self Check on page 1.*

If someone asks you what happened during your day, what do you say? You probably tell them just the most important events, not every last detail. You do the same thing when you **summarize** a text—you tell about its main idea and its key details.

Read the text below. How would you retell it to someone in a sentence or two?

Even the Toothbrush Has a History

The toothbrush has a history dating back thousands of years. Ancient Egyptians used toothbrushes made from the frayed ends of twigs. In the 1400s, the Chinese invented the first bristle toothbrush. The bristles were made from pig hairs attached to a bamboo handle. In 1938, the invention of nylon led to a modern toothbrush made of soft bristles. These improvements led to today's toothbrush, which comes in all shapes and sizes. But the basic job of the tool has not changed much. The toothbrush is still used to keep our teeth healthy and clean.

The diagram below tells you the text's main idea and three key details about it. Use these details to summarize the text. Write no more than three sentences.

Main Idea
The look of the toothbrush has changed over thousands of years.

Key Detail 1	Key Detail 2	Key Detail 3
Ancient Egyptians used toothbrushes made from the frayed ends of twigs.	In the 1400s, the Chinese invented a bristle toothbrush made from pig hairs.	In 1938, the invention of nylon led to a toothbrush made of softer bristles.

Summary: Over thousands of years, the toothbrush _____

_____

_____

Remember, a good summary tells only the main idea and the key details of a text.

Read the start of a history passage about how the English language has changed.

Genre: **History**

Changing Sounds *by James Soto*

Over the years, the English language has undergone many changes. Some words that rhymed hundreds of years ago no longer rhyme today. In fact, old rhymes often provide clues to changes in how words were pronounced.

For example, the word *sea* did not always rhyme with *see*. It originally rhymed with *say*. The sound produced by *ea* at the end of a word, as in *tea* and *pea*, shifted sometime after the 1600s. The words *speak* and *break* contain *ea* in the middle position. At one time, both words rhymed. The *ea* in *speak* sounded like the *ea* in *break*.

(continued)

Explore how to answer this question: *"How would you summarize this passage so far?"*

Read the paragraphs again. Then, on the lines below, complete the main idea, read key detail 1, and write what you think is a second key detail from the passage above.

Main idea: The sounds of words in the English language have _____.

Key detail 1: Some words that rhymed hundreds of years ago no longer rhyme.

Key detail 2: _____

_____

Now combine the main idea and key details 1 and 2 into a brief summary of the paragraph. Remember, a summary includes only the most important points of a passage.

_____

_____

_____

_____

_____

Close Reading

To summarize this part of the text, identify the most important details.

Continue reading about changes to the English language. Use the Close Reading and the Hint to help you answer the question.

(continued from page 36)

About 400 years ago, a writer named William Shakespeare wrote a poem that had lines ending in the words *speak* and *break*. The lines are shown below. Don't worry if you can't understand what Shakespeare is saying. Just look at the underlined words at the end of each line.

> Give sorrow words: the grief that does not <u>speak</u>
> Whisper the o'er-fraught heart, and bids it <u>break</u>.

These lines used to rhyme. *Speak* sounded like *spake*, and *break* sounded like it still does—*brake*. But these lines no longer rhyme because how we say *speak* has changed. In the time and place of William Shakespeare, the words *speak*, *sneak*, *beak*, and *bleak* all rhymed with *break*.

Hint

Which choice includes only key details?

Circle the correct answer.

Which of the following is the best summary of this part of the passage?

A Years ago, Shakespeare wrote rhyming verses, using words such as *speak*, *break*, *sneak*, *beak*, and *bleak*.

B Knowing about the history of words helps to understand the real meaning of Shakespeare's rhyming verses.

C The words *speak* and *break* rhymed in Shakespeare's time, but changes in pronunciation mean the words no longer rhyme.

D Word pairs should rhyme at the end of poetry verses, but many pairs do not.

✎ Show Your Thinking

 With your partner, write a summary of the entire passage on a separate piece of paper. Remember to use only the key details in your summary. Write no more than four sentences.

Read the history passage. Use the Study Buddy and the Close Reading to guide your reading.

I want to summarize this history text. Because that's my purpose for reading, I'm going to look for the main idea and key details.

Close Reading

The author organizes the passage by time periods. Find and **circle** three time periods.

Why did certain hairstyles become popular? **Underline** any sentences that tell why certain hairstyles became popular.

Genre: **History**

Hair Today, Gone Tomorrow   *by Jan Russ*

1   Just as clothing fashions change, so do hair fashions. People in the past sometimes used their hair to make unusual statements—much like today.

2   Before the invention of scissors, people just let their hair grow long and tied it back. But after a while, people began to style their hair. Some hairstyles were very complex.

3   The largest and most elaborate hairstyles appeared in the late 1700s. Women wore their hair piled high on top of their heads. As the style became even more extreme, they wove hair onto large wire frames. Some of these hairpieces towered three feet above a woman's head! The style also called for fancy ornaments. Tucked into the hairpieces were flowers, birds, and waterfalls—even complete battle scenes!

4   In the 1920s, women started a fashion of cutting hair short, called hair bobbing. Women "bobbed" their hair to show the newly independent spirit of the time. The fashion of short hair was then replaced by a return to long hair.

5   In the 1960s, many women wore their hair long and very straight. Because not everyone is born with straight hair, many teenagers would iron their hair to make it straight. They would lay their curly hair on an ironing board and press the curls straight. Soon, young men, like young women, also let their hair grow long, partly as a sign of rebellion. This rebellion was a statement against the social rules of the time—as many fashions are.

Hints

Which choice is the most important detail about hair fashion in the 1960s?

Use the Hints on this page to help you answer the questions.

1 Which of these is the best summary of the last paragraph?

A In the 1960s, all teenagers with curly hair ironed their hair to make it straight.

B In the 1960s, many young people grew long hair as a statement against the social rules of the time.

C In the 1960s, women bobbed their hair short to make a statement about their independence.

D In the 1960s, young women and men cut their hair in strange styles as a sign of anger.

Which choice is a key detail that supports the main idea?

2 Which detail is most important to put in a summary of the passage?

A The most elaborate hairstyles appeared in the late 1700s.

B Scissors have not always been around.

C Short hair is usually replaced by long hair.

D People can press their curls with an iron and an ironing board.

Imagine you have 30 seconds to tell a friend what the whole passage is about. What details should you include? What details should you leave out?

3 Write a summary of key events in the history of hairstyles. Use at least three details from the passage in your summary to support your answer.

_____

_____

_____

_____

_____

_____

_____

Read the history article. Then answer the questions that follow.

from "It All Began with *Spacewar!*"

by Peter Roop, Cobblestone

1   Two enemy spaceships slowly circled each other on a black and white screen. One spaceship accelerated as the other rotated to the right. The first spaceship fired a silent missile at its opponent. The missile missed its target. The second spaceship returned fire. Its missile hit the enemy and erased it from the screen.

2   This was the scene on the screen of *Spacewar!*, the world's first video game. This historic game ushered in the age of electronic games. . . .

3   The basic rules were quickly established: two enemy spaceships controlled by switches firing missiles at one another. The team then added stars to the background and introduced gravity and hyperspace to make *Spacewar!* more challenging and realistic.

4   *Spacewar!* was an immediate hit at computer conventions and demonstrations. It not only showed what a computer could do, but it was also fun to play.

5   Games had been played on computers long before *Spacewar!* was created. Researchers in the 1950s had programmed their "giant electronic brains" to play checkers, tic-tac-toe, and chess. Computers were so new in 1960 that nobody was certain just how many tasks these machines could perform. Games were ideal for discovering the "intelligence" of computers. . . .

6   *Spacewar!* proved too bulky and complicated for the average person to play. For years, it remained a researchers' game. Then, in 1971, Ralph Baer, an electronics engineer, began working on hooking a computer to a home television.

7   Describing his work, Baer said, "The thought came to me that you should be able to do something else with television besides watch it. You ought to be able to play games." With this idea in mind, Baer invented *Odyssey*, a game with a bouncing ball and paddles that could be played on any television screen. *Odyssey* was the first video game consumers could buy and play at home.

8   About the same time, Nolan Bushnell and Ted Dabney, two electrical engineers, designed the game *Computer Space*. Bushnell described the game as "a cosmic dogfight between a spaceship and a flying saucer." *Computer Space*, however, did not catch on with game players. So Bushnell and Dabney invented an electronic table tennis game, which they called *Pong*. An expert on arcade games, Bushnell matched the excitement of table tennis with the fun of a pinball machine. *Pong* was so successful that Bushnell founded the Atari company

to manufacture and sell the game. *Pong* is considered the first truly successful coin-operated video game.

9   The boom in video games was on! Dozens of companies entered the business of making video games for homes and arcades. *Space Invaders*, *Asteroids*, *Sea Wolf*, *Carnival*, and many other video games began thrilling players in every corner of America. . . .

10   Today, the original *Spacewar!* is on display at The Computer Museum in Boston, where everyone can see the game that helped introduce the wonders of the computer to the world.

Answer the questions. Mark your answers to questions 1 and 2 on the Answer Form to the right.

Answer Form
1 Ⓐ Ⓑ Ⓒ Ⓓ Number
2 Ⓐ Ⓑ Ⓒ Ⓓ Correct /2

1   Which detail would be **most** important to include in a summary of the article?

   A   *Spacewar!*, the world's first video game, helped introduce the computer to the world.

   B   The rules of *Spacewar!* included two enemy spaceships, which were controlled by switches firing missiles at each other.

   C   *Spacewar!* was an immediate hit at computer conventions and demonstrations.

   D   Two enemy spaceships slowly circled each other on a black and white screen.

2   Which of these details would you **not** include in a summary of the article?

   A   *Spacewar!*, the world's first video game, began the age of electronic games.

   B   Games were ideal for exploring what computers could do.

   C   *Space Invaders*, *Asteroids*, *Sea Wolf*, and *Carnival* were all arcade games.

   D   *Spacewar!* was too difficult for most people to play.

3   On the lines below, write down the main idea of "It All Began with *Spacewar!*"

_____

_____

Now, write down three key details from the article.

Key detail 1: _____

_____

Key detail 2: _____

_____

Key detail 3: _____

_____

Finally, use the main idea and the key details you wrote down above to write a summary of "It All Began with *Spacewar!*" Write your summary on the lines below.

_____

_____

_____

_____

_____

_____

 **Self Check**   *Go back and see what you can check off on the Self Check on page 1.*

Lesson 6 Part 1: Introduction 👥

Supporting Inferences About Informational Texts

CCSS

RI.4.1: Refer to details and examples in a text when explaining what the text says explicitly and when drawing inferences from the text.

Theme: *Where Foods Come From*

Imagine this. It's early morning in the spring, and you're in a park. The grass is *really* wet. You didn't see what made the grass wet, but you've got some good ideas.

- Maybe it rained during the night. It was cloudy and windy when you fell asleep.
- Maybe someone watered the grass. That could happen.

These are good ideas. Remember, you didn't actually see what made the grass wet. Instead, you used what you saw and what you know to figure out two pretty good answers. You made two **inferences**.

Now look at the cartoon below. Use what you see and what you know to make an inference about what is happening to the boy.

In the cartoon, circle details that tell you what has happened to the boy.

Now look at the diagram below. It shows how to make an inference about the cartoon.

Details from the Cartoon	➕ What You Know	＝ Inference
• A bottle of hot sauce is on the table. • The boy has food in front of him. • Smoke and fire come from his ears.	• Hot sauce is spicy! • Too much hot sauce is painful.	The boy added too much hot sauce to his food.

Reading is often like figuring out what made the grass wet or what happened to the boy in the cartoon. Reading often requires you to make inferences. Learning to make inferences is a habit of a good reader.

Read the first paragraph of a social studies passage about the potato.

Genre: **Social Studies**

The Travels of the Potato   *by Marie Schaeffer*

The potato plant is native to the Andes Mountain region of South America. This is where it first appeared and thrived. The ancient Incas were the first people known to eat the potato. It is an excellent food source, one that provides both energy and vitamins. During the 1500s, Spanish explorers to that region encountered the potato. They had never seen it before. By the 1600s, potatoes were grown in many places in Spain.

(continued)

Explore how to answer these questions: *"How did the potato get to Spain? Why was the potato grown in Spain?"*

The writer does not say how the potato got to Spain or why it was grown there by the 1600s. You need to make inferences to answer both of these questions.

The diagram below answers the question: **How did the potato get to Spain?**

Details Given	+	What You Know	=	Your Inference
• The potato is native to South America. • The Spanish saw the potato there. • By the 1600s, the potato was in Spain.		• Spain is in Europe. • An ocean is between Europe and South America. • Spanish explorers sailed between those continents.		Spanish explorers brought the potato to Spain on the boats they used to sail the ocean.

Use the diagram below to answer the question: **Why was the potato grown in Spain?**

Details Given	+	What You Know	=	Your Inference
_____		_____		_____
_____		_____		_____
_____		_____		_____
_____		_____		_____
_____		_____		_____

Continue reading about potatoes. Use the Close Reading and the Hint to help you answer the question.

Close Reading

After you read the question below, **underline** a sentence about climate. Then reread page 44 and **underline** a sentence about how well the potato grew in the Andes Mountain region.

(continued from page 44)

    Early on, some Europeans shunned the potato. Scientists learned that it was closely related to some poisonous plants. But some European doctors accepted the potato as a medicine and used it to treat common illnesses. By the early 1700s, potatoes were being raised in England as a food crop. The plants grew well in the cool, moist climate. Soon, the potato became a major food staple, particularly in Ireland. Finally, in 1719, immigrants from England and Ireland introduced the potato to the New England area of North America.

Hint

The climate of the Andes Mountain region is probably like England's.

Circle the correct answer.

Which of these is most likely the climate of the Andes Mountain region where Spanish explorers first encountered the potato?

A   warm and wet

B   warm and dry

C   cool and wet

D   cool and dry

✎ **Show Your Thinking**

Look at the answer you chose above. Explain why you chose that answer and not the others. Use details from the text in your explanation.

_____

_____

_____

_____

Read the social studies passage. Use the Study Buddy and the Close Reading to guide your reading.

I make inferences all the time. For example, the text says, "Native Americans ate a bread made with cranberries mashed into cornmeal." I know that bread is made by baking, so I can infer that Native Americans baked food.

Close Reading

Cranberries need specific conditions to grow. **Underline** two sentences telling what conditions they need.

Did Native Americans cultivate cranberries? **Draw a box** around a sentence that helps you infer an answer to that question.

Genre: **Social Studies**

Fruit of the Bog *by Alden Sims*

1   The first people known to eat cranberries were the Native Americans in northern regions of what is now the United States. Centuries before the Pilgrims arrived in 1620, Native Americans ate a bread made with cranberries mashed into cornmeal. They also munched on dried cranberries throughout the winter. But cranberries were useful for more than just food. Native Americans made dye from the berries to color blankets and rugs. And, they used the berries as a medicine for the treatment of wounds.

2   In 1810, Henry Hall from Cape Cod, Massachusetts, became the first person known to cultivate cranberries. (The word *cultivate* means "to grow as a farm crop.") Cranberries grow only in particular conditions. They grow best in bogs. They need an acid, peat soil, a steady water supply, and a covering of sand. The growing season must last from April to November, followed by a dormant period in the winter. The winter chill is needed for the fruit buds to mature.

3   For years, the number-one cranberry-producing state in the United States was Massachusetts. However, since 1995, the state of Wisconsin has been the top cranberry producer. In 2010, Wisconsin harvested more than 4 million barrels of cranberries. Do you know how cranberry farmers know when the berries are ripe and ready to harvest? The small berries float to the surface of the bog and bob along there. The farmers are able to pull off this nifty harvest trick because inside each berry is a tiny pocket of air.

Hints

What would happen to the buds if they did not get their "winter chill"?

Use the Hints on this page to help you answer the questions.

1 Read this sentence from paragraph 2 of the text.

The winter chill is needed for the fruit buds to mature.

What would most likely happen if one winter were too warm?

A People would give up growing cranberries in the area.

B Cranberries could no longer grow in the soil.

C The chill would take place in the spring.

D Most of the fruit buds would not grow properly.

Some of these choices might be true, but you need to find the only choice supported by details in the text.

2 Based on the text, which is most likely true about Wisconsin?

A It was first settled by Native Americans.

B It is a major producer of blankets and rugs.

C It provides the conditions needed for growing cranberries.

D It has always been the number-one cranberry-producing state.

Good inferences are those you can back up with words, phrases, or sentences from the text.

3 After reading "Fruit of the Bog," a student makes this inference:

Before Europeans came to North America, the cranberries that Native Americans ate were wild, not grown as a crop.

Decide if the details in the passage support this inference. State why or why not. Use at least two details from the text to support your answer.

_____

_____

_____

_____

_____

_____

_____

Read the social studies article. Then answer the questions that follow.

from "Why Salt? Valuable Little Cubes"

by Leigh Anderson and David Chandler, Appleseeds

1   Today, salt is given out freely in shakers and packets at our favorite restaurants. We can buy it cheaply at any grocery store. But it hasn't always been so easy to get salt. This tiny crystal cube has played a much more important role in history than just flavoring our fries. Around the world, cities were founded, roads were built, wars were fought, and trade routes were established, all for one reason: humans can't live without salt. Literally. Because of this simple fact, salt became a valuable item a long time ago. People who controlled salt had power. Around 2,000 years ago, some of the people with salt—and power—were the Romans.

2   One way Rome controlled salt was by building villages along the Mediterranean coast. This gave them access to the sea where they could harvest salt. One of the first great roads built by Romans . . . is called *Via Salarium*, or "Salt Road." It is the oldest road in Italy today. As you might have guessed, it was built to transport salt.

3   As Rome grew, it became a great trading center, and salt was one of the main items traded there. Salt was so important in the daily lives of the Romans that soldiers were paid in blocks of salt. This pay was called *salarium argentums* or "salt money," giving us our word *salary*. In fact, the word *soldier* comes from the Latin *sol dare*, meaning "to give salt."

4   Throughout history and around the world, governments have regulated and taxed salt. . . . Salt played a role in the history of our country, too. In both the Revolutionary and Civil wars, keeping enough salt for the soldiers was important. In these and other wars, enemies have tried to keep salt away from each other. The history of the world is overflowing with stories of salt.

What's So Important About Salt?

5   Human beings can't live without salt. It is a basic ingredient in our bodies. Salt is in our tears, sweat, saliva, blood, and even in our urine. Without this mineral our cells, nerves, and muscles can't do their jobs properly. However, too much salt can cause kidneys to work overtime, blood vessels to swell, and blood pressure to go dangerously high.

6   Our health depends on having the right amount of salt in our bodies. Generally, the human body is very good at keeping our salt levels balanced. But sometimes that balance can be thrown off. Our diets, for example, might contain extremely low or extremely high amounts of salt. If this goes on for too long, there could be serious consequences—even death.

7   When early humans survived on the meat they hunted, their bodies got enough salt from the animals they ate. As people learned to grow their vegetables and grains and began to eat less meat, salt became more important. And it was often hard to find. The need for salt and the limited supply of it made salt very valuable!

Answer Form

1 Ⓐ Ⓑ Ⓒ Ⓓ
2 Ⓐ Ⓑ Ⓒ Ⓓ   **Number**
3 Ⓐ Ⓑ Ⓒ Ⓓ   **Correct** ╱3

1   According to the article, the Romans built villages along the Mediterranean coast because

   A the coast was located near the Salt Road, an important trade route.

   B the Romans could afford to build beautiful villages there.

   C the Romans wanted to control and harvest salt.

   D Roman soldiers were paid in blocks of salt.

2   Which sentence from the article **best** supports the idea that salt costs much less today than it did earlier in history?

   A "Today, salt is given out freely in shakers and packets at our favorite restaurants."

   B "This tiny crystal cube has played a much more important role in history than just flavoring our fries."

   C "Around 2,000 years ago, some of the people with salt—and power—were the Romans."

   D "Our health depends on having the right amount of salt in our bodies."

3   Read this sentence from the article.

> Salt was so important in the daily lives of the Romans that soldiers were paid in blocks of salt.

Based on this sentence, what conclusion can you draw?

A   The soldiers did not have a healthy diet, so they were paid in blocks of salt.

B   Salt was so valued by the Romans that it was used as a form of money.

C   The Roman government ran out of gold, so it paid soldiers in blocks of salt.

D   The soldiers traded blocks of salt for items they needed on the Salt Road.

4   Explain how the value of salt has changed since the time of the ancient Romans. Include at least **two** details from the article to support your answer.

_____

_____

_____

_____

_____

_____

_____

_____

_____

_____

✓ **Self Check**   *Go back and see what you can check off on the Self Check on page 1.*

Read the history article. Then answer the questions that follow.

from "And Away We Go: Rockets"

from Kids Discover

1   From blastoff to touchdown, a rocket is an awesome sight. The Saturn 5 Rocket that sent astronauts to the moon stood 363 feet high, about the height of a 30-story building, and weighed more than six million pounds. With rocket engines, it sent a spacecraft weighing more than 100,000 pounds to a lunar landing.

2   In 1930, Robert Goddard, a Massachusetts-born scientist working almost totally alone, was the first to set earthlings on a path out of this world and into space. Thirty-nine years after Goddard shot off his first rocket, United States astronaut Neil Armstrong took his first step on the moon. Since that time, rockets have lifted

The Chinese invented rockets more than 1,000 years ago. The first rockets were tubes packed with gunpowder. In the 1200s, Chinese soldiers fired them at their enemies.

A rocket is a type of engine. It produces more power for its size than any other type of engine. A rocket can produce about 3,000 times more power than a car engine of the same size.

hundreds of spacecraft and satellites into orbit around Earth. They have carried space shuttles to and from the *International Space Station.* They have sent unmanned spacecraft to Mars and Jupiter. Satellites put in orbit by rockets beam back information about Earth's atmosphere and weather.

3   Robert Goddard once called himself a "one-dream-man." His dream was to send a rocket into space. It began on October 19, 1899, when he was 17 years old. He climbed a ladder to trim branches from a cherry tree. As he looked up, he had a vision of traveling into space.

4   Throughout his career, Goddard worked mostly alone, with little money or support. Rocket research was not considered a proper subject for a serious scientist, so Goddard experimented with rockets in his free time. Most of his experiments took place on his aunt's Massachusetts farm.

Robert Goddard on March 16, 1926, holding the launch frame for a rocket of his own design.

Up, Up, and Away!

Launch a rocket in your backyard with these simple household materials.

Materials: empty quart or liter bottle, cork, paper towels, 3 or 4 streamers (made from paper towels or crepe paper), thumbtack, 1/2 cup water, 1/2 cup vinegar, 1 teaspoon baking soda.

Directions:

1. Make your rocket by attaching streamers to the top of the cork with the thumbtack. Make sure the cork will fit tightly into the bottle. If it is too 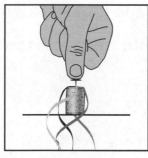 tight, ask an adult to help you trim the cork with a knife. If it's too loose, wrap pieces of paper towel around it until it fits snugly in the bottle top.

2. With the cork out of the bottle, put the water and the vinegar into the bottle.

3. Cut a 4-inch by 4-inch piece of paper towel. Wrap the baking soda in the paper towel, twisting the ends to keep the baking soda in.

4. Go outside where there is plenty of space. Drop the paper-towel-wrapped baking soda into the bottle. Fit the cork into the bottle top. Set the bottle upright away from any people.

5. WAIT. As the liquid soaks through the paper towel, the vinegar will react with the baking soda and produce carbon dioxide gas. As more  and more gas forms, the pressure will build up inside the bottle. Eventually, the bottle will blow its cork. The streamers will help you trace its flight.

1 According to Step 5 in "Up, Up, and Away!," rocket-makers need to wait

A to make sure that the cork fits tightly in the bottle.

B for the vinegar to react with the baking soda to produce gas in the bottle.

C until the bottle is brought outside and is pointed away from people.

D until the baking soda is wrapped into the paper towel.

2 Read this sentence from paragraph 3 of the article.

Robert Goddard once called himself a "one-dream-man."

What did Goddard mean by this?

A Throughout his career, Goddard worked mostly alone.

B Most of his experiments took place on his aunt's Massachusetts farm.

C In 1899, Goddard climbed a cherry tree and looked up into space.

D His main goal was to send a rocket into space.

3 Which of the following **best** states the author's purpose in writing "And Away We Go: Rockets"?

A to inform the reader about Robert Goddard and his contributions to rocket research

B to convince the reader to support future rocket research

C to entertain the reader with a childhood memory about visiting a farm in Massachusetts

D to describe for the reader the size of the Saturn 5 Rocket

4 Which statement from the article explains why Robert Goddard experimented with rockets only in his free time?

  A " . . . he had a vision of traveling into space."

  B " . . . his experiments took place on his aunt's Massachusetts farm."

  C "Rocket research was not considered a proper subject for a serious scientist. . . ."

  D " . . . was the first to set earthlings on a path out of this world and into space."

5 Answer Parts A and B below.

Part A

The first instruction in "Up, Up, and Away!" tells rocket-makers to attach streamers to the top of the cork. Why are the streamers important?

  A They bring liquid into the bottle.

  B They help people follow the flight of the cork.

  C They make the cork fit tightly into the bottle top.

  D They react with the baking soda and vinegar to make gas.

Part B

Which sentence from the text **best** supports the answer to Part A?

  A "The streamers will help you trace its flight."

  B "As the liquid soaks through the paper towel, the vinegar will react with the baking soda and produce carbon dioxide gas."

  C "Make your rocket by attaching streamers to the top of the cork with the thumbtack."

  D "Make sure the cork will fit tightly into the bottle."

6 Which of the following explains why the cork will blow out of the bottle?

    A   Gas forms and builds up pressure inside the bottle.

    B   The paper towel absorbs the vinegar and builds up pressure in the bottle.

    C   The vinegar makes the cork expand, which then seals the bottle tightly.

    D   The streamers pull the cork away from the top of the bottle.

7 The sentence below is from Step 1 of "Up, Up, and Away!"

    Make sure the cork will fit tightly into the bottle.

Why is it important for the cork to fit tightly? What would happen if it didn't fit tightly? Use details from the procedure to support your answer.

_____

_____

_____

_____

_____

_____

_____

_____

Performance Task—Extended Response

8 What is a rocket? What are some of the jobs that rockets have done throughout history? Use details from the article to support your answer.

In your answer, be sure to include
• a description of what a rocket is
• some of the jobs rockets have done in the past
• some of the jobs rockets do now
• details from the article to support your answer

Check your writing for correct spelling, grammar, capitalization, and punctuation.

_____

_____

_____

_____

_____

_____

_____

_____

_____

_____

Unit 2
Key Ideas and Details in Literature

When you read stories, plays, and poems, what do you notice first? Most likely it's **details** about the characters, settings, and events. For example, imagine you tell a friend about the book *Tales of a Fourth-Grade Nothing*. First, you might talk about Peter and his little brother, Fudge. Then you might tell how Fudge does things that make Peter angry. Next, you might talk about an important event in the story, like when Fudge writes all over Peter's project poster. Finally, you might tell your friend that the book shows how Peter comes to like his little brother. Learning how to live with others—even people who annoy you—is a **key idea** of that book.

In this unit, you'll learn how and why readers pay attention to characters, settings, and events. You'll see that careful reading means paying close attention to what the characters think, say, and do. Finally, you'll practice summarizing the key ideas of a text and figuring out its theme.

✓ Self Check

Before starting this unit, check off the skills you know below. As you complete each lesson, see how many more you can check off!

I know how to:	Before this unit	After this unit
describe characters by referring to their thoughts, words, and actions.	☐	☐
use details from a story or play to describe a setting or an event.	☐	☐
figure out the theme of a story or play.	☐	☐
explain how a theme is supported by details.	☐	☐
summarize a story, play, or poem.	☐	☐
refer to details and examples when explaining and inferring what a story, play, or poem is telling you.	☐	☐

Describing Characters in Plays

CCSS
RL.4.3: Describe in depth . . . a character . . . in a . . . drama, drawing on specific details in the text (e.g., a character's thoughts, words, or actions).

Theme: *Adventure Plays*

Characters are the people, animals, or made-up creatures in a story or drama (a play). You can learn about characters by paying attention to how they look and what they say, think, and do.

What do the characters look like, say, think, and do in this cartoon?

Circle clues that tell you Edmund is afraid of the dog.

Read the diagram below. It shows how you can learn what characters are like based on their appearance, actions, words, and thoughts. You can make and use a diagram like this when you need to describe characters.

Character's Name		
Edmund		

Physical Description	**Actions**	**Words and Thoughts**
• big, strong-looking alien	• hiding behind a tree • biting his fingernails	"What kind of furry monster is that?"

If you want to get to know the characters in a drama, pay close attention to the details about them. The characters in a play might be nice, mean, funny, or bored, but you will only know this by what they say, do, and think. When you pay attention to details about characters, you will better understand them.

Read the first part of a play about two kids searching for a buried treasure.

Genre: **Play**

The Treasure *by Mabel Astor*

1   [*Setting:* Iris *and* Gus, *a brother and sister, are in a forest.* Iris *holds a map.*]

2   Iris [*studying the map*]: We're supposed to turn left up here by that big tree.

3   Gus [*nervous*]: But it's getting dark, and we told Mom we'd be back for dinner.

4   Iris: Seriously, Gus? We're searching for buried treasure! The world won't end if we get home a little late.

5   Gus [*nodding his head*]: Yeah, I guess you're right . . . .

6   Iris: That's more like it. Let's get going! We can't let Victor and Elsa beat us.

(continued)

Explore how to answer this question: *"Gus is unsure about something. What is it?"*

Look for details in the play to help you answer the question. Then complete the diagram below.

Character's Name
Gus

Words	**Actions**
• "But it's getting dark, and we told Mom _____." • "Yeah, _____."	• He feels _____. • He nods _____.

Tell what Gus is unsure about. Support your answer using details you wrote in the chart.

_____

_____

_____

_____

Continue reading the play. Use the Close Reading and the Hint to help you answer the question.

Close Reading

Gus says he is afraid of heights. Find and **underline** what Iris says in response to Gus.

(continued from page 62)

7 [*They keep going. A sudden wind blows the map from* IRIS's *hand.*]

8 IRIS: Oh no! The map! [*The wind whisks the map into a tree.*]

9 GUS: What are we going to do now?

10 IRIS: I guess one of us is going to have to climb up there.

11 GUS: But I'm afraid of heights.

12 IRIS [*shivering*]: I am, too, but do you think I'm going to let that stop us? [*She takes a deep breath and starts climbing.*]

13 GUS: Look! [*points to a gold coin in the dirt under the tree*]

Hint

Which choice explains why Iris climbs the tree?

Circle the correct answer.

In this scene, what do Iris's actions show about her?

A She is mad that Gus won't get the map.

B She doesn't give up easily.

C She isn't really afraid of heights.

D She enjoys climbing trees.

✎ **Show Your Thinking**

Which details from the play helped you answer the question above?

_____

_____

_____

💬 Pick an answer you did not choose. Tell your partner why that answer does not describe Iris. Use details from the play to explain your answer.

Read the play. Use the Study Buddy and the Close Reading to guide your reading.

When I read a play, I try to picture in my mind what happens on stage. This includes how characters say their lines. Doing that helps me figure out what the characters are like.

Close Reading

The officer tells William to shoot an apple from the head of his son. Why does William react angrily? **Underline** a detail that tells why he reacts angrily.

What kind of person is William? **Circle** three details (such as words, actions, or thoughts) that show what kind of person he is.

Genre: **Play**

William Tell   *adapted from a Swiss folktale*

1   [*Setting: A busy marketplace in Altdorf, Switzerland*]

2   WILLIAM: Come, my son. I have sold the cowhides. Now we must buy the things your mother has asked us to get.

3   ALBERT: Yes, Father. And what about a toy for little Lewis?

4   WILLIAM: You are a good boy to remember your little brother.

5   OFFICER: Stop, man! Why do you not salute the cap of your king! [*The* OFFICER *points to a pole. On top is a cloth cap. It belongs to the Austrian king, who has conquered Switzerland.*]

6   WILLIAM: I love my country. But I refuse to honor the Austrian king, who forces suffering upon my people.

7   OFFICER: Then I'll arrest you as a traitor! What is your name?

8   WILLIAM [*standing tall*]: William Tell.

9   OFFICER: And this is your son? [*looks to a nearby* SOLDIER] Soldier! Tie the boy to that tree over there!

10 WILLIAM: Leave him be! He is only a child!

11 OFFICER: I hear you are a famous shot. Perhaps you can shoot an apple from the head of your son? If so, I will let you go free.

12 WILLIAM: Never, you villain! I would rather die than risk hurting him. Now let him go, and take me to jail!

13 OFFICER: You will both die unless you shoot the apple as I say.

14 WILLIAM [*thinking aloud*]: Oh, dear life, what am I to do?

15 ALBERT [*trembling*]: Father, I want to go home.

16 WILLIAM: Stand still, my brave boy. I promise I'll not hurt you. [*He shoots, and then he falls to his knees, sighing with relief.*]

17 SOLDIER: The apple is split! That was a fine shot!

18 OFFICER [*frowning*]: I did not believe anyone could make it. I suppose I must honor my word and set you free.

Hints

> A kind person does nice things for other people.

Use the Hints on this page to help you answer the questions.

1 Which detail from the play shows that Albert is kind?

　A　He goes with his father to the marketplace.

　B　He wants to get a toy for his little brother.

　C　He trembles after the soldier ties him to a tree.

　D　He tells his father that he wants to go home.

> What could happen if William misses the shot?

2 Read these lines from the play.

> OFFICER: I hear you are a famous shot. Perhaps you can shoot an apple from the head of your son? If so, I will let you go free.

What do these lines show about the officer?

　A　He keeps his promises.

　B　He is loyal to the king.

　C　He is cruel and uncaring.

　D　He likes playing games.

> How does William treat his son? How does he act toward the officer?

3 Describe the character of William Tell. Support your answer with at least three details from the play about what William says, does, or thinks.

_____

_____

_____

_____

_____

_____

_____

_____

Read the play. Then answer the questions that follow.

Robin Hood and the Sad Knight

adapted from an English folktale

[Scene 1: ROBIN HOOD and his men are making arrows in the woods.]

1 LITTLE JOHN: How I long for a good meal after today's work.

2 ROBIN HOOD: Me, too. But not before we find a wealthy traveler to pay the bill. Little John, ride out and find us one.

3 LITTLE JOHN: With pleasure, my master.

4 ROBIN HOOD: Remember, do not bring a farmer or a worker. Those who toil for what they have shall live in peace. Bring only those who are cruel to the poor and the weak.

5 WILL SCARLET: Look! [*pointing*] A knight! But he looks so sad and walks so slowly.

6 *[Enter the KNIGHT. His face is tired, and his clothes are dirty.]*

7 ROBIN HOOD: Welcome, gentle knight. I am Robin Hood. Will you not join us for dinner? We have meats of pheasant, swan, and deer.

8 KNIGHT: I have not eaten for days. If I come again to this forest, I will repay your kindness.

9 ROBIN HOOD: Sorry, Sir Knight. Here in the forest, our rich guests must pay for their food.

10 KNIGHT: I wish that I could pay you, but I have no money.

11 ROBIN HOOD: Is that the truth? Little John, check his bags.

12 LITTLE JOHN [*searches the KNIGHT's bags*]: Indeed, the knight speaks the truth.

13 ROBIN HOOD: Why is it you are so poor? Tell us your story.

14 KNIGHT [*sits on a fallen tree*]: A year ago, I had plenty of money. But then my son got in a quarrel and to save him, I pledged all my lands. Unless I pay four hundred pounds by next week, I shall lose them all.

15 ROBIN HOOD: Have you no friends to help you in your need?

16 KNIGHT: I had friends when I had money, but now when I need their help, they turn away.

17 ROBIN HOOD: Gentle knight, we are your friends. Little John, go to the chest and count out four hundred pounds.

18 WILL SCARLET: Shall he not have cloth for a coat? His clothes are badly worn.

19 ROBIN HOOD: Of course. Give him a length of our finest fabric.

20 LITTLE JOHN: Here is the money, good knight.

21 KNIGHT [*smiling*]: Many thanks. Tell me, Robin Hood, when shall I come to repay the money you have so kindly lent?

22 ROBIN HOOD: This day twelve months from now, we will meet under this tree. Till then, be merry!

23 KNIGHT: I will be here. Thank you and farewell, my new friends.

[Scene 2: The KNIGHT returns home after his long journey.]

24 LADY LEA: Oh, my dear husband! How glad I am to see you!

25 KNIGHT: I am happy to see you and to share my good news! I must tell you how kind my friend Robin Hood has been to me.

26 LADY LEA [*confused*]: Robin Hood? Your friend? Is he not the outlaw of the forest?

27 KNIGHT: Yes, but he is a good man. He gave me the money to regain our lands. In a year, we will go to the forest and repay him.

28 LADY LEA: I shall be glad to meet him and his merry men!

---

1 What does Will Scarlet say that shows he wants to help the knight?

A He points out the knight coming through the woods.

B He asks if they can give the knight cloth for a coat.

C He notices that the knight walks slowly.

D He describes the knight as looking sad.

Answer Form

1 Ⓐ Ⓑ Ⓒ Ⓓ
2 Ⓐ Ⓑ Ⓒ Ⓓ   **Number**
3 Ⓐ Ⓑ Ⓒ Ⓓ   **Correct** /3

2 Which sentence supports the idea that Robin Hood is good to people who need help?

A "Here in the forest, our rich guests must pay for their food."

B "We have meats of pheasant, swan, and deer."

C "Have you no friends to help you in your need?"

D "Little John, go to the chest and count out four hundred pounds."

3 Read these lines from the play.

> LADY LEA [*confused*]: Robin Hood? Your friend? Is he not the outlaw of the forest?

What do these lines show about Lady Lea?

A She is surprised her husband knows Robin Hood.

B She has never heard of Robin Hood before.

C She thinks Robin Hood has no friends at all.

D She is anxious to meet Robin Hood and his men.

4 Explain how the knight changes from the beginning of the play to the end. Include at least **two** details from the play to support your answer.

_____

_____

_____

_____

_____

 **Self Check** *Go back and see what you can check off on the Self Check on page 59.*

Lesson 8   Part 1: Introduction 👥

Describing Settings and Events in Stories

CCSS

RL.4.3: Describe in depth a . . . setting or event in a story . . . drawing on specific details in the text. . . .

Theme: *Stories About Families*

The **setting** of a story is where and when it takes place. A story's **events** are the things that happen, such as winning a contest, going to the park, or riding on a space ship.

Look at the photos below. What details tell you about the settings? What details tell you about the events?

Now read the table below. It shows you how paying attention to details can help you describe settings and events. Complete the last column.

Photo	Details	Setting	Event
Left	man, child, trees, grass, daylight, soccer ball	**Where?** a park **When?** daytime	**What is happening?** _____ _____ _____
Right	woman, children, snow, cold, trees, snowman, daylight	**Where?** outside **When?** winter, daytime	**What is happening?** _____ _____ _____

When you pay attention to details about setting and events, you'll get more out of the stories you read. For example, you might see how one event leads to another event. Or, you might see how the setting of a story affects what happens in the story.

Read the first two paragraphs of a story about two siblings whose grandma is coming to visit.

Genre: **Realistic Fiction**

Meeting Grandma   by Gillian Adams

Several years ago, when I was about seven, my grandma came to visit us. That summer, it was so blazingly hot, we never got to go outside. We were thrilled to go with our dad to pick her up from the airport.

The airport was a new experience to my brother and me. We rushed excitedly from one shop to another, fascinated by all the things one could buy. Then we turned our attention to the restaurants. We pleaded for a pretzel, ice cream, a cold drink, anything.

(continued)

Explore how to answer these questions: *"What is the setting of this story? What are the main events in this part of the story?"*

You can answer these questions by looking at the details the author provides.

Look for details that tell about the setting and events. Then fill in the blanks in the table.

Setting	Events
When did it happen? several years ago during a blazingly hot summer	**What happened first?** The family goes to pick up Grandma from the airport.
Where did it happen? Describe the place, using details from the text.	**What happened next? Describe what happened next, using details from the text.**
We turned our attention to the restaurants. fascinated by all the things one could buy.	*We rushed excitedly from one shop to another. We pleaded for a pretzel, ice cream, a cold drink, anything.*

What do the details tell you about the setting and the events? They tell you when and where the story takes place. The details also show how the children behave when they get there.

Continue reading the story about the siblings who meet their grandma at the airport. Use the Close Reading and the Hint to help you answer the question.

Close Reading

Write a number next to each sentence that tells an event in this part of the story. **Label** the first event with a "1," the second event with a "2," and so on.

(continued from page 70)

Our parents finally agreed to buy us a fruit smoothie. We thought carefully about the flavors—blueberry, strawberry, banana, what to choose? After a while, we made up our minds and ordered. But then the server was o-so-slow in preparing the drinks. But finally we got them, sat down, and began drinking them up. They were really cold, so we took our time.

That is where Grandma found us. We had completely lost track of time. Grandma's plane had arrived, and worried that we were lost, she had come in search of us.

Hint

How would you describe the ending of the story to a friend?

Circle the correct answer.

Which sentence describes the last event in the story?

A   The server takes a long time.

B   Grandma finds her family.

C   Everyone thinks about the flavors.

D   Grandma worries her family is lost.

Show Your Thinking

Describe how the children in the story react to the setting. How does their reaction help you learn more about these characters?

Their reaction helps us because we know this because that in they begging they love smoothies and they were very happy and they get very worried in the exlit day

How do the early events in the story lead to the end of the story? Describe the events that cause Grandma to come looking for the family. They early event in the story Lead to the end of the story because they early they were all happy and show the worries. And soon thing that caused grandma to close them is because they were to call and that her to have

Read the story. Use the Study Buddy and the Close Reading to guide your reading.

Genre: **Realistic Fiction**

Where does the story take place? What details tell me this? Does the setting ever change? If it does change, how come? These are some questions I ask myself when reading fiction.

Baseball Lessons   *by Anita Gomez*

1   Elena slammed the door hard. For weeks she had been asking her brothers to teach her how to play baseball, and they had said they would. But today, when she asked to join a game, Jorge said no. "Go away, little one," he said. "This game is for expert players." How dare he call her little one!

2   She wandered into her kitchen. There, her grandmother was busy making the evening meal. She threw her backpack down. "Jorge and Hector won't let me play baseball with them. Abuela, you have to make them let me play."

3   Abuela looked up and said, "Elena, I didn't know you played baseball." Elena admitted she didn't know how, but she wondered how she could learn unless someone showed her. "You're in luck," smiled Abuela. "I used to be quite the pitcher in my day. We'll have a practice session outside."

4   For the next two weeks, they practiced in the backyard. Abuela taught Elena everything she knew about baseball, and that was a lot. Finally, she sent Elena off to find a game.

5   Elena found her brothers and their friends in a game at the park. When she asked to join in, Jorge tried to send her away, but one of his friends threw Elena a long, high ball. Reaching up with her glove, she made the catch easily. "Wow!" said Jorge. "How did you learn to catch like that?"

6   "Abuela taught me. I can throw hard and run fast too."

7   "Well, if Abuela taught you, you must be good. She taught Hector and me too," he laughed. "Welcome to the game."

Close Reading

What happens when Jorge's friend throws Elena a high ball? **Circle** the words that tell whether it's hard for her to make the catch.

Jorge changes his mind at the end of the story. **Underline** one event that leads him to do so.

Hints

All of the choices suggest that the story starts at a home. But which choice shows that it's Elena's home?

Use the Hints on this page to help you answer the questions.

1 Which detail best shows that the first part of the story takes place inside Elena's home?

  A "Elena slammed the door hard."

  B "She wandered into her kitchen."

  C "She threw her backpack down."

  D "Elena found her brothers and their friends in a game at the park."

Which choice tells how Elena shows off her new baseball skills?

2 Read these sentences from the story.

> When she asked to join in, Jorge tried to send her away, but one of his friends threw Elena a long, high ball. Reaching up with her glove, she made the catch easily.

Which sentence best describes this event?

  A Elena goes to the park to play baseball.

  B Elena puts on her glove so she can play catch.

  C Elena catches the baseball with little effort.

  D Elena practices catching the baseball with a glove.

At first, Jorge thinks Elena will not be a good player. Look for ways Elena shows him he is wrong.

3 Describe two events that change Jorge's mind about letting Elena play. Use at least two details from the story to support your answer.

_____

_____

_____

_____

_____

_____

_____

Read the story. Then answer the questions that follow.

King Lear

by William Shakespeare. Retold by E. Nesbitt in Beautiful Stories of Shakespeare

1   King Lear was old and tired. He was aweary of the business of his kingdom, and wished only to end his days quietly near his three daughters. . . .

2   Lear called his three daughters together, and told them that he proposed to divide his kingdom between them. "But first," said he, "I should like to know much you love me."

3   Goneril, who was really a very wicked woman, and did not love her father at all, said she loved him more than words could say; she loved him dearer than eyesight, space or liberty, more than life, grace, health, beauty, and honor.

4   "I love you as much as my sister and more," professed Regan, "since I care for nothing but my father's love."

5   Lear was very much pleased . . . and turned to his youngest daughter, Cordelia. "Now, our joy, though last not least," he said, "the best part of my kingdom have I kept for you. What can you say?"

6   "Nothing, my lord," answered Cordelia.

7   "Nothing can come of nothing. Speak again," said the King.

8   And Cordelia answered, "I love your Majesty according to my duty—no more, no less."

9   And this she said, because she was disgusted with the way in which her sisters professed love, when really they had not even a right sense of duty to their old father.

10   "I am your daughter," she went on, "and you have brought me up and loved me, and I return you those duties back as are right and fit, obey you, love you, and most honor you."

11   Lear, who loved Cordelia best, had wished her to make more extravagant professions of love than her sisters. "Go," he said, "be forever a stranger to my heart and me." He divided the kingdom between Goneril and Regan, and told them that he should only keep a hundred knights at arms, and would live with his daughters by turns. . . .

12   The King now went to stay with his daughter Goneril, who had got everything from her father that he had to give, and now began to grudge even the hundred knights that he had reserved for himself. She was harsh and undutiful to him, and her servants either refused to obey his orders or pretended that they did not hear them. . . .

13   "Goneril," said Lear, "I will not trouble you further—yet I have left another daughter."

14   And his horses being saddled, he set out with his followers for the castle of Regan. But she, who had formerly outdone her sister in professions of attachment to the King, now seemed to outdo her in undutiful conduct, saying that fifty knights were too many to wait on him, and Goneril . . . said five were too many, since her servants could wait on him.

15   Then when Lear saw that what they really wanted was to drive him away, he left them. It was a wild and stormy night, and he wandered about the heath half mad with misery. . . .

16   Here [Cordelia and her friends] found poor King Lear, wandering about the fields, wearing a crown of nettles and weeds. They brought him back and fed and clothed him, and Cordelia came to him and kissed him.

17   "You must bear with me," said Lear; "forget and forgive. I am old and foolish."

18   And now he knew at last which of his children it was that had loved him best, and who was worthy of his love. . . .

Answer the questions. Mark your answers to questions 1–3 on the Answer Form to the right.

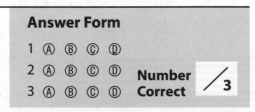

Answer Form

1 Ⓐ Ⓑ Ⓒ Ⓓ
2 Ⓐ Ⓑ Ⓒ Ⓓ   **Number**   /3
3 Ⓐ Ⓑ Ⓒ Ⓓ   **Correct**

1   Read this sentence from the story.

> And now he knew at last which of his children it was that had loved him best, and who was worthy of his love. . . .

Which key detail from the story shows who loves King Lear **best**?

A   "'I love you as much as my sister and more,'" professed Regan, "'since I care for nothing but my father's love.'"

B   "'Now, our joy, though last not least,' he said, 'the best part of my kingdom have I kept for you.'"

C   "Lear, who loved Cordelia best, had wished her to make more extravagant professions of love than her sisters."

D   "They brought him back and fed and clothed him, and Cordelia came to him and kissed him."

2 At the end of *King Lear*, the setting helps show how unhappy Lear has become. Which sentence from the story **best** shows this?

A "He was aweary of the business of his kingdom, and wished only to end his days quietly near his three daughters. . . ."

B "And his horses being saddled, he set out with his followers for the castle of Regan."

C "It was a wild and stormy night, and he wandered about the heath half mad with misery. . . ."

D "'You must bear with me,' said Lear; 'forget and forgive. I am old and foolish.'"

3 Read this sentence from the story.

But she, who had formerly outdone her sister in professions of attachment to the King, now seemed to outdo her in undutiful conduct. . . .

Which sentence **best** describes what happens in the sentence above?

A King Lear tells Cordelia to leave his kingdom and his heart.

B King Lear realizes that Regan treats him worse than Goneril did.

C King Lear is pleased at how much his daughters claim to love him.

D King Lear sets off along on a wild and stormy night.

4 Early on, Cordelia says, "I love your Majesty according to my duty—no more, no less." Explain how King Lear's understanding of Cordelia's words changes over time. Use at least **two** details from the story to support your answer.

_____

_____

_____

_____

 **Self Check** *Go back and see what you can check off on the Self Check on page 59.*

Lesson 9   Part 1: Introduction 👥

Determining the Theme of a Story

CCSS

RL.4.2: Determine a theme of a story . . . from details in the text.

Theme: *Tales of Bravery*

In a story, a **theme** is a message or a lesson about how to live in the world and act toward other people. Normally, an author does not tell you the theme directly. Instead, you need to figure out the theme by paying attention to what the characters say and do and what happens to them.

Read the cartoon below. Try to figure out a message about life it expresses.

Now, tell how the character feels at the beginning and the end of the cartoon.

First, the character feels _____.

At the end, the character feels _____.

Read the table below. It shows how you can use details to figure out a theme.

Finding the Theme		
How Do the Characters Act?	**What Are the Main Events?**	**What Lessons Are Told?**
The boy is scared, then happy.	• The boy fears the waterslide. • He goes down anyway. • He decides waterslides are fun, not scary.	• It takes courage to try new things. • Facing your fears can be rewarding.

When you figure out a theme, you'll have a deeper understanding of the characters and events you're reading about. You will also have learned an important idea about life, such as "Help those who help you" or "making new friends can be fun."

Read the start of a story about two travelers.

Genre: **Fable**

The Two Travelers   *adapted from a fable by Aesop*

Two men planned a trip that would take them through wild, lonely country. They promised that if they met with danger they would stand by each other.

"To the end!" said the first man.

"To the end!" said the second man.

They traveled only a short distance when a bear rushed out of the woods at them. The first man, as soon as he saw the bear, rushed to a tree and climbed it as quickly as he could. The other man, who was slower to see the bear, realized he had no time to escape. He fell to the ground, pretending to be dead.

(continued)

Explore how to answer this question: *"Based on the events so far, what theme do you think this story will have?"*

To figure out a theme, look for important details about the main events and the characters. Then ask yourself how those details might be trying to teach a lesson of some kind.

The table below lists details from the story. Use the blank lines to complete the table.

What Are the Main Events?	What Do the Characters Do?
• Two men promise to stand by each other when in danger. • When a bear runs out of the woods, the first man *he rushed to a tree and climbed It as quickley as he could*. • The second man pretends *to be dead*.	The first man is unkind to the second man by not keeping his promise and leaving the second man alone with the bear.

Now predict what theme this story will have. Use details from the table in your answer.

I predict that the theme of the story will be. That you should always be brave and not scared1 man 2 Man you should never lie you should always tell the truth

Continue reading about the two travelers. Use the Close Reading and the Hint to help you answer the question.

Close Reading

How does the second man feel about what the first man has done? **Underline** a sentence that shows how the second man feels.

(continued from page 78)

The bear came over to the man on the ground. The animal sniffed and smelled the traveler. The bear put his face right up to the man's ear. But the man held his breath and soon, losing interest, the bear walked away.

When the bear was safely out of sight, the first traveler slid down the tree and walked over to his companion, who was now sitting by the side of the road.

"Well, that was a close one, wasn't it?" the first man said. "What did that bear say when he had his mouth to your ear?"

"It's no secret," growled the second man. "He said I should never again believe anything said by a coward like you!"

Hint

What lesson do you learn from how the first man treats the second?

Circle the correct answer.

What is the theme of this story?

A Bears aren't as dangerous as people think they are.

B Wise people don't believe everything their friends say.

C True friends stand by each other even in times of danger.

D Be thankful when someone does something nice for you.

✎ **Show Your Thinking**

Look at the answer you chose above. Explain how details in the story helped you figure out the theme of "The Two Travelers."

I picked this answer because man 1 was looking and he saw a bear and went up the tree and left the man behind.

Read the story. Use the Study Buddy and the Close Reading to guide your reading.

When I want to identify a theme, I focus on what the characters say and do. This helps me figure out the lesson the author wants to get across.

Close Reading

What do the girls do with the tacks? What is the result? **Underline** sentences answering these questions.

How do the girls make a difference? **Draw a box** around a sentence that shows this.

Genre: **Historical Fiction**

Claudine's Tack Attack   *by Nadine Blanc*

1   For three long years, the Nazis had occupied France. Everyone in my village was used to German trucks driving through, carrying ammunition and supplies to the front to supply the Nazi soldiers in their battles against the American soldiers. From her window, my friend Claudine and I would glumly watch the trucks roar and rumble by.

2   "Too bad we can't slow them down," I said one day.

3   Claudine's eyes became thoughtful. "Maybe we can!" She shared her idea, and we ran to her father's workshop.

4   "These might work," she announced, holding out a can of long blue steel tacks. "Papa uses them to shingle roofs."

5   Heading back to the road, I had second thoughts. How could two twelve-year-olds slow down a war machine with a bunch of tacks? Still, I followed Claudine up the hill to a spot above the road. We crouched behind an old stone wall.

6   We didn't have to wait long. Two trucks rolled into view. "Like this," whispered Claudine. She flung a handful of the tacks onto the road, and then I threw a handful too. When all the nails were gone, we ducked out of sight. Blam! The exploding tire sounded like a gunshot. Then another. Blam!

7   "Two blowouts!" Claudine whispered as we crept away. After dark, we strolled out toward the road. The German soldiers were still struggling with the heavy tires. Better yet, the road was so narrow that no other trucks could pass. Claudine and I delayed twelve trucks for half the day!

Hints

> The girls want to slow down the trucks. But why is this important?

1 Why are the trucks driving through the girls' village?

- **(A)** They're bringing supplies to Nazi soldiers.
- **B** They're trying to get away from the fighting at the coast.
- **C** They're heading back to Nazi Germany.
- **D** They're carrying soldiers to fight the Americans.

> Which sentence tells how the girls slow down the German soldiers?

2 What do the girls do to help the American soldiers?

- **A** They figure out where the German soldiers are going.
- **B** They crouch behind a wall and watch for the German trucks.
- **C** They go near the road after dark and spy on the Germans.
- **(D)** They throw tacks in the road and delay the German trucks.

> Think about the actions the girls take. Which action shows the most courage? How does that action make a difference?

3 The central theme of the story is that small acts of courage can make a difference. Write a paragraph explaining the key points that support this theme. Use at least two details from the story to support your response.

Two key details that support our theme are "Claudine and the they asterf tal valent soldiers.

Read the story. Then answer the questions that follow.

from "Sir Ivaine"

by Maude L. Radford, in King Arthur and His Knights

1   Among Arthur's Knights of the Round Table was one who was a mixture of good and bad, as indeed most people are. His name was Sir Ivaine; brave, kind-hearted, and merry; but at the same time fickle, sometimes forgetful of his promises, and inclined to make light of serious things.

2   One night, in the early spring, the knights and ladies of Arthur's Court were sitting in the dining-hall. The king and Guinevere had withdrawn, but were expected to return. Supper had been served. . . . Four little pages in blue and white velvet kirtles sat on stools watching the fire, and perhaps dreaming of the days when they, too, should be warriors and have adventures.

3   Sir Ivaine was telling of his experience with the Black Knight.

4   "It was when I was very young," he said; "indeed, I had just been made a knight. Some one told me of the wicked Black Knight who lived, and still lives, in a wood a long way from here. Knowing that he did much evil, I determined to kill him. I rode to the wood where he lived. . . .

5   "Then a great storm of wind and rain arose, and when it was at its height the Black Knight rode up and began to attack me. We fought for a little while, but he easily overthrew me. Thinking me dead, he rode back, leaving me on the ground. But after a time I was able to mount my horse, and went back to my mother's castle."

6   At this moment the king and the queen entered, unperceived by any one except Sir Ivaine. The young man, who was always polite, sprang to his feet; then the other knights rose. Sir Kay, who was not always sweet-tempered, said to Sir Ivaine:

7   "We all know that you are very polite, but you have more courtesy than bravery."

8   At that Sir Ivaine said: "I was almost a boy when the Black Knight overthrew me, but I could conquer him now."

9   "It is very easy to say that after you have eaten," said Sir Kay. "Almost any knight feels brave and self-satisfied when he has had a good supper of venison."

10   The king asked what the conversation was about, and Sir Ivaine repeated the story of his adventure, adding: "And, Sir King, I crave your permission to set forth to-morrow to slay this Black Knight who is a pest in the land."

11   "I have heard of this man," said the king, "and have often thought of sending some one to punish him. But he lives far away, and it has been necessary heretofore to right first the wrongs nearest home. Yet now his evil deeds and persecutions must cease. To-morrow a company of us will set forth and conquer him and all his people."

12   The king named some half-dozen of his knights, Sir Ivaine among them, who were to undertake this adventure.

13   Sir Ivaine was displeased; he thought that the adventure should be his alone. So he rose in the middle of the night and stole away unattended, determined to go in advance of the others and kill the Black Knight. It did not occur to him that in proving himself brave, he was also proving himself disobedient. . . .

Answer the questions. Mark your answers to questions 1 and 2 on the Answer Form to the right.

Answer Form
1 Ⓐ Ⓑ Ⓒ Ⓓ   **Number**
2 Ⓐ Ⓑ Ⓒ Ⓓ   **Correct** ╱2

1   Read this sentence from the passage.

> Sir Kay, who was not always sweet-tempered, said to Sir Ivaine: "We all know that you are very polite, but you have more courtesy than bravery."

Which sentence from the story shows how Sir Ivaine tries to prove Sir Kay wrong?

A   "His name was Sir Ivaine; brave, kind-hearted, and merry; but at the same time fickle, sometimes forgetful of his promises, and inclined to make light of serious things."

B   "'Then a great storm of wind and rain arose, and when it was at its height the Black Knight rode up and began to attack me.'"

C   "'And, Sir King, I crave your permission to set forth to-morrow to slay this Black Knight who is a pest in the land.'"

D   "The king named some half-dozen of his knights, Sir Ivaine among them, who were to undertake this adventure."

2   Which sentence from the story **best** suggests that Sir Ivaine will learn a lesson?

     A   "Among Arthur's Knights of the Round Table was one who was a mixture of good and bad, as indeed most people are."

     B   "'I have heard of this man,'" said the king, 'and have often thought of sending some one to punish him.'"

     C   "Sir Ivaine was displeased; he thought that the adventure should be his alone."

     D   "It did not occur to him that in proving himself brave, he was also proving himself disobedient. . . ."

3   Sir Ivaine is inexperienced when he first battles the Black Knight. Find **one** sentence from the story that is evidence for this claim. Write it below.

_____

_____

4   Sir Kay tells Sir Ivaine, "Almost any knight feels brave and self-satisfied when he has had a good supper of venison."

Explain what Sir Kay is suggesting about Sir Ivaine's character. Use at least **one** detail from the passage to support your answer.

_____

_____

_____

_____

_____

 **Self Check**   *Go back and see what you can check off on the Self Check on page 59.*

Lesson 10   Part 1: Introduction 👥

Determining the Theme of a Poem

CCSS
RL.4.2: Determine a theme of a . . . poem from details in the text. . . .

Theme: *Where Roads Can Take You*

A poem's **theme** is a message or lesson that the poet wants to get across to the reader. The message or lesson is usually about how to live or act. Poets don't usually state a theme directly. Instead, you have to figure it out from details in the poem.

Read the poem. What lesson do you think the reader can learn from the poem?

A Fork in the Road
The road down which to go,
I simply do not know.
How do I make up my mind
When I know not what I'll find?

On the lines below, tell what lesson you think the reader can learn from the poem.

The lesson they are trying to teach us is. That Making up your mind can be difficult

Read the table below. It shows how you can use a poem's details to find its theme.

Finding the Theme of a Poem		
What Is It About?	**What Does It Describe?**	**What Do You Learn?**
A person is trying to decide which way to go.	A person can't decide which way to go. The person doesn't know where the roads lead.	Making decisions in life can be difficult.

When you can figure out a poem's theme, that poem will take on greater meaning—and you'll have a lot more fun reading, talking, and writing about it, too!

Read the first part of a poem about roots.

Genre: **Lyric Poem**

Roads   *by Rachel Field,* Favorite Poems, Old and New

A road might lead to anywhere,—
    To harbor towns and quays,
Or to a witch's pointed house
    Hidden by bristly trees.
It might lead past the tailor's door,
    Where he sews with needle and thread,
Or by Miss Pim the milliner's,
    With her hats for every head.

(continued)

Explore how to answer this question: *"Based on what you have read so far, what do you think is the theme of 'Roads'?"*

To figure out the theme of a poem, think about what the poem describes. Then ask yourself how those details might connect to a message or lesson you can take away from the poem.

Look back at the details in the poem and what they describe. Then answer the questions.

What is the poem mostly about? The poem is about the different places roads can take you.

What does the poem describe? The poem describes roads going different places. These

places include _____.

What message or lesson do you think the poem is giving, at least so far?

_____

_____

_____

_____.

Continue reading this poem about roads. Use the Close Reading and the Hint to help you answer the question.

Close Reading

Do these roads take the reader to normal places or special places? Both here and on page 86, **underline** places that seem special.

(continued from page 86)

It might be a road to a great, dark cave
    With treasure and gold piled high,
Or a road with a mountain tied to its end,
    Blue-humped against the sky.
Oh, a road might lead you anywhere—
    To Mexico or Maine.
But then, it might just fool you, and—
    Lead you back home again!

Hint

The poem isn't just about roads. It's also about the unexpected. Which choice describes this theme?

Circle the correct answer.

Which sentence best describes the theme of this poem?

A You never know where life will take you.

B Traveling is the best way to learn about the world.

C Some places are more interesting than others.

D Don't let people fool you into going the wrong way.

✎ **Show Your Thinking**

Look at the answer you chose above. What details helped you figure out which sentence describes the theme of the poem "Roads"?

_____

_____

_____

 Pick an answer you did not choose. Tell your partner why that sentence is not the theme of "Roads" based on the details and descriptions in the poem.

Read the poem. Use the Study Buddy and the Close Reading to guide your reading.

The speaker says that he wants to "be a friend to man." Are there also details that tell me what kind of person the speaker does not want to be?

Close Reading

How does the speaker show he wants to help people at all times? **Underline** two lines that show this.

How does the speaker feel about being mean to other people? **Draw a box** around two lines that show his feelings.

Genre: **Lyric Poem**

The House by the Side of the Road

by Sam Walter Foss, Dreams in Homespun

Let me live in a house by the side of the road
    Where the race of men go by—
The men who are good and the men who are bad,
    As good and as bad as I.
I would not sit in the scorner's seat[1]
    Nor hurl the cynic's ban[2]—
Let me live in a house by the side of the road
    And be a friend to man.

I see from my house by the side of the road,
    By the side of the highway of life,
The men who press with the ardor of hope,
    The men who are faint with the strife,
But I turn not away from their smiles nor their tears,
    Both parts of an infinite plan—
Let me live in a house by the side of the road
    And be a friend to man.

[1] **sit in the scorner's seat:** think bad things about other people

[2] **hurl the cynic's ban:** say mean things about other people

Hints

What do you know about the speaker by the end of the poem? That will help you understand these first two lines.

Use the Hints on this page to help you answer the questions.

1 Read these lines from the poem.

> Let me live in a house by the side of the road
> 　Where the race of men go by—

What do these lines show about the speaker?

A He doesn't mind living on a noisy street full of traffic.

B He wishes to spend his life close to other people.

C He likes watching a running race that goes by his house.

D He prefers a quiet life over being part of a busy world.

Which choice includes words about helping other people?

2 Which line from the poem best shows that the speaker would rather help other people than avoid them?

A "I would not sit in the scorner's seat"

B "I see from my house by the side of the road"

C "By the side of the highway of life"

D "But I turn not away from their smiles nor their tears"

Look back at the parts you underlined to find ideas in the poem that help to show the theme.

3 The central theme of the poem is that it is good to accept people as they are. Write a paragraph explaining the key points that support this theme. Use at least three details from the poem to support your response.

three details from the It supports the It that it is good to accept people as they are. I know this because it says "I would not sit in the scorner seat." But I turn not away from their smiles nor their tears". "let me live in a house by the side of the road where the race of men go by."

Read the poem. Then answer the questions that follow. *topic events*

The Beach Road by the Woods

by Geoffrey Howard, from A Treasury of War Poetry

I know a beach road,
    A road where I would go,
It runs up northward
    From Cooden Bay to Hoe;
5 And there, in the High Woods,
    Daffodils[1] grow.

And whoever walks along there
    Stops short and sees,
By the moist tree-roots
10   In a clearing of the trees,
    Yellow great battalions[2] of them,
    Blowing in the breeze.

While the spring sun brightens,
    And the dull sky clears,
15 They blow their golden trumpets,
    Those golden trumpeteers!
They blow their golden trumpets
    And they shake their glancing spears.

And all the rocking beech-trees
20   Are bright with buds again,
And the green and open spaces
    Are greener after rain,
And far to southward one can hear
    The sullen, moaning rain.

[1] **Daffodils:** a bright, yellow flower that grows along beaches and woods
[2] **Battalions:** a large group of troops who are ready for battle

25 Once before I die
     I will leave the town behind,
  The loud town, the dark town
     That cramps and chills the mind,
  And I'll stand again bareheaded there
30   In the sunlight and the wind.

  Yes, I shall stand
     Where as a boy I stood
  Above the dykes and levels[1]
     In the beach road by the wood,
35 And I'll smell again the sea breeze,
     Salt and harsh and good.

  And there shall rise to me
     From that consecrated[2] ground
  The old dreams, the lost dreams
40   That years and cares have drowned:
  Welling up within me
     And above me and around
  The song that I could never sing
     And the face I never found.

[1] **Dykes and levels:** *Dykes* are walls built to prevent the sea from flooding the *levels*, which are flat areas of land.
[2] **Consecrated:** holy, blessed

Answer Form

1 Ⓐ Ⓑ Ⓒ Ⓓ
2 Ⓐ Ⓑ Ⓒ Ⓓ **Number**
3 Ⓐ Ⓑ Ⓒ Ⓓ **Correct**   /3

1   What kind of place is the beach road in the poem?

    A   It is where people walk along playing golden trumpets.

    B   It is where the speaker spent time during his childhood.

    C   It is often loud, dark, and windy.

    D   It is where the speaker once dreamed about being a singer.

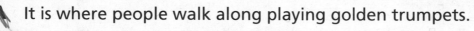

2   Which sentence **best** describes how the speaker feels about the beach road and the area around it?

    A   He likes it except when it's too rainy and windy.

    B   It's a beautiful, happy place that he misses greatly.

    C   The sea breeze makes him want to sing with joy.

    D   It's a nice place to visit, but he prefers life in town.

3   Which sentence **best** describes a main theme of the poem?

    A   People are as happy as they make up their minds to be.

    B   A cheerful attitude can turn any place into one you love.

    C   You shouldn't wish for things that you can't have.

    D   Special places bring back strong memories of better times.

4   Another main theme of this poem is "The joys and hopes of childhood are often lost but not forgotten." Describe how the poem expresses this theme. Include at least **two** details from the poem to support your explanation.

The theme is always rember your
Best childhood I know this because
"Once before I die I will
the town behind "the old dreams
the lost dreams"

✓ **Self Check**   *Go back and see what you can check off on the Self Check on page 59.*

Summarizing Literary Texts

CCSS
RL.4.2: . . . summarize the text [of a story or drama].

Theme: *Tales of Confusion*

When you **summarize** a text, you retell its most important details and events. A summary is a shorter version of the full text. A good summary answers some or all of these questions: *Who? What? Where? When?* and *Why?*

Read the story below. Think about how you would retell it to someone in a sentence or two.

A Jacket in the Boot

We were visiting my parents' friends in England. Their son James and I became fast friends. One afternoon, he and I decided to go to the park. It was cool outside, so James was looking for his jacket. Then he said, "Oh, I think I left it in the boot." I looked at him, puzzled. Why would he leave his jacket in a boot?

James started laughing. Then he told me that in England, the trunk of a car is called a *boot*. We had taken a drive to the countryside earlier. Because it had been warmer then, he had left his jacket in the trunk instead of wearing it.

Complete the table below to help you see what details to include in a summary. Then, complete the summary on the lines provided in the table.

Who?	What?	Where?	When?	Why?
An American boy and an English boy	The American boy gets confused.	*Park in England*	*One afternoon*	He doesn't know that boot means "trunk" in England.

Summary: An American boy is visiting England. He doesn't know what the word *boot* means in that country. As a result, *he felt confused and did not know the word (boot) because he was not from there.*

When you summarize a work of fiction, you sort out its most important parts—and that gives you a better grasp of what the story is all about.

Read the start of a story about a girl who agrees to do a favor for her mom.

Genre: **Realistic Fiction**

The Mix-Up   *by Frank Auster*

Jenna told her mom she was going to take a bike ride around the neighborhood. "Great!" said her mom. "Could you deliver these packages for me? This one is for your great aunt Sally, and this one is for your cousin Joey." Her mom explained that Sally and Joey had birthdays coming up next week.

"No problem," said Jenna. They lived in a small town, so no one lived far from each other. Jenna tucked the packages in her backpack and headed out.

(continued)

Explore how to answer this question: *"How would you summarize what's happened in the story so far?"*

Remember, a summary includes only the most important details and events.

Reread the passage. Look for details someone needs to know to understand what has happened so far. Fill in the details on the lines provided.

Who is in the story so far? <u>Mom, Jenna, Sally, Joey</u>

Where does the story take place? <u>in her house and outside</u>

When does this part of the story take place? This part of the story takes place during the

week before Sally and Joey's <u>birthdays.</u>

What has happened so far? Jenna is going out for a <u>bike ride.</u>,

and Jenna's mom asks Jenna to <u>deliver a package to sally and Joey.</u>

On the lines below, use the details you wrote down to write a summary of the story so far.

<u>Jenna was about to go for a bike ride</u>
<u>in a small tow but them her Mom said can you</u>
<u>deliver these packages to Sally and Joey Jenna</u>
<u>Said yes and took them.</u>

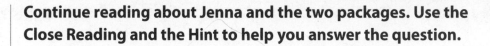

Continue reading about Jenna and the two packages. Use the Close Reading and the Hint to help you answer the question.

Close Reading

When does Jenna realize she gave Sally the wrong present? **Underline** what Jenna sees that shows her the mistake she made.

(continued from page 94)

When Jenna arrived at Sally's house, she realized neither package had a name on it. But she was sure Sally's was the one in the striped wrapping paper. She gave her the present and then dropped off Joey's.

The following week, Sally invited Jenna and her mom over for lunch. Sally answered the door wearing a baseball jersey. "How did you know this is my new favorite team?" she said smiling.

"Oh, just a guess," said Jenna's mom. She glared at Jenna, who quickly recognized her mistake.

Hint

Which choice tells only the most important details to know?

Circle the correct answer.

Which is the best summary of this part of the story?

A Jenna arrives at Sally's house and realizes neither package is labeled, but she is sure the striped one is Sally's.

B When Jenna and her mom go over to Sally's for lunch, Sally opens the door wearing a baseball jersey.

C Jenna mixes up the packages but doesn't realize until later, when Sally is wearing the present that was for Joey.

D Jenna gives Sally the present in the striped paper, which turns out to be a baseball jersey of her favorite team.

✎ **Show Your Thinking**

Look at the answer you chose. Explain how you figured out which details best sum up what happens in this part of "The Mix-Up."

I figered out this am a mix up is she seen Sally wearing the jersy. they got a realized the name was not on the package.

Read the play. Use the Study Buddy and the Close Reading to guide your reading.

When I summarize a text, it helps to imagine a friend is asking me, "Well, what's it all about?" If I give too many details, my answer might be longer than the original text!

Close Reading

At whom do the men think the rider is laughing? **Draw boxes** around the words that tell whom each man believes the rider is laughing at.

Why do the men touch the elephant in the first place? **Underline** the sentences that tell why the men touch the elephant.

Genre: **Play**

The Blind Men and the Elephant
based on an Indian folktale

1   [*Four blind men stand by a road. A man on an elephant rides by.*]

2   RIDER: Out of the way! I must take my elephant by.

3   FIRST MAN: I have never seen an elephant, sir.

4   OTHER MEN: Nor I!

5   RIDER: Do you know what he is like?

6   ALL FOUR MEN: No, sir.

7   RIDER: Come, then, stand by him, and touch him.

8   FIRST MAN [*placing his hand on the elephant's side*]: Well, well! Now I know all about him! He is exactly like a wall!

9   SECOND MAN [*feeling the tusk*]: He is not like a wall! He is round and smooth and sharp. He is like a spear.

10 THIRD MAN [*feeling the trunk*]: No, no! He is like a snake.

11 FOURTH MAN [*feeling a leg*]: Oh, how wrong you are! He is round and tall like a tree! [*All four men start arguing.*]

12 RIDER: Ha, ha, ha! [*He rides on, laughing.*]

13 FIRST MAN: Ha, ha, ha! Hear how he laughs at you all!

14 SECOND MAN: He laughs at you and the others.

15 THIRD MAN: He laughs not at me!

16 FOURTH MAN: I say he laughs at you and the others!

17 [*The four men shake their fingers angrily and shout at each other.*]

Hints

A summary tells what is most important. It does not, however, give too many details.

Use the Hints on this page to help you answer the questions.

1 Which sentence summarizes what happens when the men touch the elephant?

A Each man touches a different part of the elephant and so has a different idea of what an elephant is like.

B One man thinks the elephant is like a wall, another thinks he is like a spear, and another thinks he is like a snake.

C The third man touches the elephant's trunk and says the elephant is like a snake, not a wall, a spear, or a fan.

D The first man says he knows all about the elephant, but the third and fourth man tell him he is wrong.

Which choice is true of what all the men say after the rider leaves?

2 Which sentence is the best summary of what the men say to each other toward the end of the play?

A The first three men agree the rider is laughing at what the fourth man has just said.

B Each man believes the rider is laughing not at him but at the other men.

C All of the men are sure the rider is laughing because what they have each said is incorrect.

D All four of the men insist that what they have each said is the truth in its own way.

Think about the most important parts of the play. How could you explain to someone in just a few sentences what the play is about?

3 On the lines below, summarize the events of the play.

Some of the men have never seen a Elephant. So they had to touch them and everybody started laughing because they were talking about a Elephant. they thought It was a wall they thought It was round and smooth.

Read the fable. Then answer the questions that follow.

The Two Frogs

a Japanese fable

1   Once upon a time in the country of Japan, there lived two frogs. One made his home in a ditch near the town of Osaka, on the sea coast, while the other dwelt in a clear little stream that ran through the city of Kioto. At such a great distance apart, they had never even heard of each other. But funnily enough, the idea came into both their heads at once that they should like to see a little more of the world. After much thought, the frog who lived at Kioto decided he wanted to see Osaka and the sea, and the frog who lived at Osaka decided he wanted to go to Kioto, where the great Mikado had his palace.

2   So one fine morning in the spring, they both set out along the road that led from Kioto to Osaka, one from one end and the other from the other. The journey was more tiring than they expected, for they did not know much about traveling, and half way between the two towns, there arose a mountain that had to be climbed. It took them a long time and a great many hops to reach the top, but there they were at last, and what was the surprise of each to see another frog before him!

3   They looked at each other for a moment without speaking and then fell into conversation, explaining the cause of their meeting so far from their homes. It was delightful to find that they both felt the same wish—to learn a little more of their native country—and as there was no sort of hurry, they stretched themselves out in a cool, damp place and agreed that they would have a good rest before they parted to go their ways.

4   "What a pity we are not bigger," said the Osaka frog, "for then we could see both towns from here and tell if it is worth our while going on."

5   "Oh, that is easily managed," returned the Kioto frog. "We have only got to stand up on our hind legs and hold on to each other, and then we can each look at the town we are traveling to."

6   This idea pleased the Osaka frog so much that he at once jumped up and put his front paws on the shoulders of his friend, who had risen also. There they both stood, stretching themselves as high as they could and holding each other tightly so that they might not fall down. The Kioto frog turned his nose toward Osaka, and the Osaka frog turned his nose toward Kioto. But the foolish things forgot that when they stood up, their great eyes lay in the backs of their heads, and that though their noses might point to the places to which they wanted to go, their eyes beheld the places from which they had come.

7   "Dear me!" cried the Osaka frog, "Kioto is exactly like Osaka. It is certainly not worth such a long journey. I shall go home!"

8   "If I had had any idea that Osaka was only a copy of Kioto, I should never have traveled all this way," exclaimed the frog from Kioto. As he spoke, he took his hands from his friend's shoulders, and they both fell down on the grass. Then they took a polite farewell of each other and set off for home again. And to the end of their lives, they believed that Osaka and Kioto, which are as different to look at as two towns can be, were as alike as two peas.

---

1 Which sentence is the **best** summary of what happens in paragraph 6?

Answer Form

1 Ⓐ Ⓑ Ⓒ Ⓓ
2 Ⓐ Ⓑ Ⓒ Ⓓ   **Number Correct** /2

A Neither frog remembers that his eyes lay near the back of his head instead of toward the front.

B Both frogs stand on their hind legs and stretch as high as they can, but they are disappointed by what they see.

C The Kioto frog turns his nose toward Osaka, and the Osaka frog turns his nose towards Kioto.

D The frogs' eyes look backward when they stand up, so each frog ends up looking at the town he came from.

2 Which sentence is the **best** summary of paragraphs 7 and 8?

A The Kioto frog says that if he knew Osaka was a copy of Kioto, he would never have gone on his journey.

B The Osaka frog says that Kioto is like Osaka, and the Kioto frog says that Osaka is like Kioto.

C The frogs think the city they are traveling to is just like their hometown. They turn around and go home, never learning that Osaka and Kioto are different.

D The frogs take their hands from each other's shoulders and fall on the grass. They tell each other goodbye and set off for their hometowns.

3 In the table below, write down the most important details from "The Two Frogs."

Who Is in the Story?	Where and When Does It Take Place?	What Do the Characters Do?	Why Do They Do It?

Now use details from the table to write a summary of the story.

_____

_____

_____

_____

_____

_____

_____

✓ Self Check *Go back and see what you can check off on the Self Check on page 59.*

Lesson 12 Part 1: Introduction 👥

Supporting Inferences About Literary Texts

CCSS
RL.4.1: Refer to details and examples in a text when explaining what the text says explicitly and when drawing inferences from the text.

Theme: *Tales of the Unexpected*

An **inference** is an "educated guess," or a guess based on what you know and the details of what you see or read. When you make an inference about what you read, your inference must be supported by details you find in the text.

Look at the cartoon below. How does the girl eventually feel about the movie? What details tell you this?

Now read and complete the table below. It shows how you can make an inference based on details and what you already know.

Details from the Cartoon	**+**	What I Know	**=**	Inference
• The girl thinks about how she's excited to see the movie. • Half an hour into the movie, the girl is yawning and checking her watch. • By the end, the girl is asleep.		• Some people check their watch when they want something to be over. • People sometimes yawn and fall asleep when they think something is boring.		_____ _____ _____ _____ _____

Good readers make inferences so they can figure out things that a story doesn't say directly. Just make sure to support your inferences with specific details from the text!

Read the first two paragraphs of a story about a family and their pet parakeet.

Genre: **Mystery**

The Penny Thief   *by Charlotte Fairchild*

My family got a parakeet on the very day that we moved into our new apartment. On our first night in the new place, we tried to name our new pet. I wanted to call it Tweetie, but no one else liked that name. We couldn't find a name that everyone agreed on, so we agreed to think about it for a while.

My father always emptied his pocket change into an old clear glass jug in the hallway. When we wanted money for this or that, he would count it out for us from the jug. The very next night, as he tossed his change into the jug, he mumbled, "Funny! I'm sure there were mostly pennies on top." None of us knew where the pennies had gone.

(continued)

Explore how to answer this question: *"Based on the story so far, what do you think is happening to the pennies?"*

The author doesn't tell readers what is happening to the pennies. You need to make an inference based on details in the story and what you might already know.

Look for details that tell what is happening to the pennies. Then fill in the blanks in the table.

Details from the Story ➕	What I Know 🟰	Inference
• The family gets a parakeet when they move into their apartment. • The narrator's dad notices that _____ _____. • No one in the family knows _____ _____.	• Parakeets are birds • Most birds can fly. • Parakeets are small, and they could probably fit through the opening in a jug.	What do you think is happening to the pennies? _____ _____ _____ _____

Continue reading about the family, parakeet, and missing pennies. Use the Close Reading and the Hint to help you answer the question.

Close Reading

How could the bird have stolen the pennies? Find and **underline** the sentence that tells how it could have stolen them.

(continued from page 102)

Every day that week, my father complained that someone was taking pennies from his jug. We all pleaded ignorance. And every day that week, we discussed a new name for our pet.

At the end of the week, we took everything out of the birdcage to clean it. In every corner of the cage was a pile of pennies! That's when we learned that my mother had let the bird out to fly around every morning. "Penny thief!" my father cried. And our pet was named on the spot.

Hint

Just because pennies are in the birdcage doesn't mean the bird put them there. Which choice tells how it's possible that the bird was the penny thief?

Circle the correct answer.

Which sentence from the story explains how it could be the parakeet who put the pennies in the birdcage?

A "Every day that week, my father complained that someone was taking pennies from his jug."

B "At the end of the week, we took everything out of the birdcage to clean it."

C "In every corner of the cage was a pile of pennies!"

D "That's when we learned that my mother had let the bird out to fly around every morning."

✎ **Show Your Thinking**

Look at the answer that you chose above. Explain how the details in the answer tell you how the parakeet could be the penny thief.

_____

_____

 Pick an answer you did not choose. Tell your partner why the details in that sentence do not tell how the parakeet could be the penny thief.

Read the story. Use the Study Buddy and the Close Reading to guide your reading.

I always put my inferences through two tests. First: Is it based on details in the text? Second: Does it make sense? If my answers are "yes," then my inference is a good one.

Close Reading

How does Miek react after the flower first "speaks"? **Underline** a sentence that shows his reaction.

Why doesn't Shaundra cut the flower? **Draw a box** around a sentence telling why Shaundra stops herself from cutting the flower.

Genre: **Science Fiction**

Thinking Out Loud   *by Ben Karlsen*

1   Shaundra slipped off the helmet of her space suit and took a breath. As she had hoped, air filled her lungs. It was true: This planet, which she and her crew had spied from the mother ship, had an atmosphere like Earth's. And because it had air, perhaps it was like Earth in other ways. Was it possible that she, Miek, and Goran had found what humans had long sought? Could there be intelligent life here?

2   For hours, the three astronauts wandered through forests and meadows filled with flowers of every color, shape, and smell. But the astronauts were disappointed. They saw nothing that looked like Earth animals—not even the tiniest insect. Certainly, they met no creature with a human form.

3   Finally they returned to their landing site. Before entering the mother ship, they had to collect samples of the plants. Shaundra grasped the stem of a particularly lovely flower and placed her knife against it. Suddenly, her eyes opened wide. "Did you hear that?" she asked the other two. "Well, I don't mean *hear*, exactly. It was as if this flower spoke to my mind. It seemed to be asking me not to harm it."

4   Miek was about to tease Shaundra when his jaw dropped. "I heard it—no, I *felt* it. It wants to know where we come from and why we're here. How can we answer it?"

5   "It's obvious," replied Shaundra. "We need only to think our answers, and this creature will understand. This planet is full of intelligent life—and it's beautiful life, too."

Hints

> The astronauts infer that the planet might have intelligent life. On what detail do they base their inference?

Use the Hints on this page to help you answer the questions.

1 Which sentence from the story explains why the astronauts think they might find intelligent life on the planet?

   A "And because it had air, perhaps it was like Earth in other ways."

   B "They saw nothing that looked like Earth animals—not even the tiniest insect. "

   C "Before entering the mother ship, they had to collect samples of the plants."

   D "Shaundra grasped the stem of a particularly lovely flower and placed her knife against it."

> Which choice tells what happens when the astronauts find that the intelligent life is not what they expect?

2 Which sentence from the story best supports the inference that the astronauts expect intelligent life to look and act a certain way?

   A "Shaundra slipped off the helmet of her space suit and took a breath."

   B "As she had hoped, air filled her lungs."

   C "Was it possible that she, Miek, and Goran had found what humans had long sought?"

   D "Miek was about to tease Shaundra when his jaw dropped."

> In the last paragraph, how does Shaundra's description of the flower show how she feels about it?

3 Based on details from the story, make an inference about how Shaundra feels toward the intelligent life they discover on the planet. Include at least two details from the story to support your answer.

_____

_____

_____

_____

_____

_____

Read the story. Then answer the questions that follow.

They Glow by Night

by Lorrie Doyle

1   My name is Aimee. My real name is Amy, but I prefer Aimee. It's more original and seems kind of French. Sometimes when I write Aimee, I use a little heart to dot the *i*, but I think I might be growing out of that. I am, after all, almost ten.

2   You would think an almost-ten-year-old wouldn't need a baby-sitter, but then again, you're not my parents. They were convinced that I still needed a sitter. "It's your money," I keep telling them. "If you want to throw it away on a baby-sitter, that's up to you."

3   Anyway, Emily's not so bad. Sometimes we actually have fun. (She always brings a supply of the newest shades of nail polish for me to try.) But on this particular night, I was having a hard time concentrating on the "Glowing Green Goddess" Emily was applying to our fingers and toes. Outside, it was pouring rain. Lightning flashed across the sky, and thunder cracked so loudly it seemed to be going off right in the living room. I could feel myself getting more and more nervous—not for myself, of course. I was worried about my parents being out in the storm.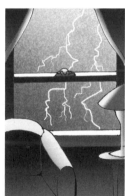

4   Just as Emily was finishing my right pinky toe, there was a flash of lightning. It was followed by the loudest crack of thunder I'd ever heard. The television went blank and silent. The hallway light went out too. I noticed the familiar hum of the refrigerator was missing. The house was completely dark and silent. Emily went to the window and looked out.

5   "All the street lights are out. None of the other houses have lights either. The power must be out in the whole neighborhood." She bumped her way over to the phone and picked up the receiver. "No dial tone," she said glumly. "The telephone lines must be down too." She stopped and thought for a moment. "Your parents must have a flashlight around here somewhere. Do you know where it is?"

6   Before I could tell her I had no idea where the flashlight was, I started to cry. Yes, it's true. I cried, I wailed, I boo-hooed like a baby. I had my hands over my eyes to stop the flow, and still the tears kept coming. We were stuck here in the dark and quiet forever. And, to top off my fear and misery, what did I hear? Emily! Laughing! That was the last straw.

7   "Here we are," I sobbed, "stranded in the dark. With my parents lost, no doubt, in the storm, and you're laughing!"

8 "Look, Amy," she said. She reached out for my hand. And there, glowing in the dark, were my ten fingernails. And down at my feet were my ten glowing toenails. I looked over at Emily. Her toes and fingers were all aglow too! "Glowing Green Goddess" was fluorescent!

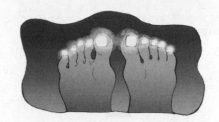

9 "See, we're not completely in the dark!" she said. "We've got our toes and our fingers to guide us. At least we won't bump into each other. Here, get the bottle of nail polish. We'll look for the flashlight by the light of 'Glowing Green Goddess.'"

10 And we did. We found the flashlight, but we didn't even use it. We preferred getting around the house by "toe-light." My parents eventually got home, and the electricity and the telephone came back on. But ever since that night, I have kept an extra bottle of "Glowing Green Goddess" around. You never know when you might need some polish power!

Answer Form

1 Ⓐ Ⓑ Ⓒ Ⓓ
2 Ⓐ Ⓑ Ⓒ Ⓓ
3 Ⓐ Ⓑ Ⓒ Ⓓ
4 Ⓐ Ⓑ Ⓒ Ⓓ   **Number Correct** /4

1 Which sentence from the story explains why Amy isn't having fun when Emily paints her nails?

   A "You would think an almost-ten-year-old wouldn't need a baby-sitter."

   B "I was worried about my parents being out in the storm."

   C "The house was completely dark and silent."

   D "And there, glowing in the dark, were my ten fingernails."

---

2 Which sentence from the story explains why Emily starts laughing after the power goes out?

   A "Emily went to the window and looked out."

   B "I cried, I wailed, I boo-hooed like a baby."

   C "We were stuck here in the dark and quiet forever."

   D "'Glowing Green Goddess' was fluorescent!"

3   Read these sentences from the story.

> Anyway, Emily's not so bad. Sometimes we actually have fun. (She always brings a supply of the newest shades of nail polish for me to try.)

Based on these sentences, with which statement would Amy **most likely** agree?

A   The only good thing about Emily is that she brings nail polish.

B   Emily always picks out the best shades of nail polish.

C   Although Emily is a likable person, she charges too much to baby-sit.

D   Emily is a nice baby-sitter who thinks of amusing things to do.

4   Which sentence from the story shows that Amy isn't as grown-up as she thinks she is?

A   "Sometimes when I write Aimee, I use a little heart to dot the *i*, but I think I might be growing out of that."

B   "I could feel myself getting more and more nervous—not for myself, of course."

C   "Before I could tell her I had no idea where the flashlight was, I started to cry."

D   "But ever since that night, I have kept an extra bottle of 'Glowing Green Goddess' around."

5   Make an inference about how Amy feels about needing a baby-sitter **after** the events of this story. Include **two** details from the story to support your answer.

_____

_____

_____

_____

_____

✓ **Self Check**   *Go back and see what you can check off on the Self Check on page 59.*

Read the following story. Then answer the questions that follow.

from *The Moffats*

by Eleanor Estes

1   [Jane Moffat] watched Mr. Brooney, the grocery man, drive up with his horse and wagon. The Moffats called Mr. Brooney's horse the dancey horse, because of the graceful way he threw his legs about when he cantered up the street. Mr. Brooney stopped between Mrs. Squire's house and the yellow house. He threw down the heavy iron weight to keep his horse from dancing away and took several baskets of groceries from the wagon. He crossed the street and disappeared in Mrs. Frost's back yard. He was gone a long time. The horse stood there with the greatest patience. Occasionally he flicked his long tail to rid himself of a pesky fly. Or now and then he wriggled an ear when Sylvie, who was practicing her graduation music, hit a high note. And sometimes he raised one dainty foot or another and then planted it firmly on the ground. For the most part, however, he stood there dreamily, looking neither to left nor to right.

2   Jane watched him and watched him.

3   He had wings and could carry her away.

4   He was the wooden horse of Troy and many men could step out of him.

5   He was a bridge that she could walk under.

6   Sitting up there on the hitching post, watching the horse and watching the horse, Jane repeated to herself, "The horse is a bridge for me to walk under, and I'm goin' to walk under it."

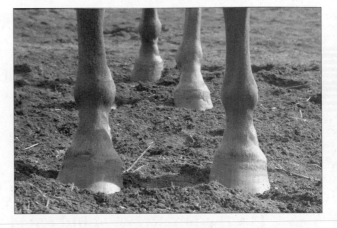

7   So she jumped down and marched over to the horse. He stood there immobile. Except for his eyes, which followed her around like those of the velvet-clad lady in the picture in the sitting-room.

8   Jane walked under him and came out on the other side. This gave her an extraordinary feeling of satisfaction and elation.

9   At that moment when Jane was walking under the horse, Mama came to the window of the front parlor and shook her duster out vigorously. "Thank heavens!" she said to herself. "Thank heavens, it's spring again and that long hard winter is over." No more fussing with stoves and wondering where the next coal was coming from, she thought, slapping the duster against the green shutters. . . .

10 But goodness! Could Mama believe her eyes? What was Janey doing? Walking under that horse! Of all things! Mama was speechless with amazement and dropped the duster out of the window at the sight. Joe and Rufus saw her from the other side of the yard and became all tangled up in their stilts in consequence. Sylvie, who was practicing her singing way back in the kitchen, was the only one who did not see her.

11 "Jane! Whatever on earth!" Mama cried. "You mustn't do such things. You mustn't walk under horses. They might kick or start walking or something."

12 Jane stepped thoughtfully up the walk. "All right, Mama," she said.

13 She had no desire to keep on walking under horses. It was just something she felt she had to do at that moment, just that once. And she knew that horse. She'd been watching him and watching him. So she had walked under him and from the feeling inside of her she thought it had turned out to be an all right sort of thing to do—just that once.

---

1 Why do the Moffats call Mr. Brooney's horse "the dancey horse"?

A The horse needs a heavy iron weight to keep him from dancing away.

B The horse stands still for a long time waiting for Mr. Brooney.

C The horse occasionally flicks his long tail to get rid of a fly.

D The horse throws his legs in a graceful way when he canters up the street.

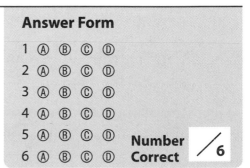

Answer Form

1 Ⓐ Ⓑ Ⓒ Ⓓ
2 Ⓐ Ⓑ Ⓒ Ⓓ
3 Ⓐ Ⓑ Ⓒ Ⓓ
4 Ⓐ Ⓑ Ⓒ Ⓓ
5 Ⓐ Ⓑ Ⓒ Ⓓ   **Number**   /6
6 Ⓐ Ⓑ Ⓒ Ⓓ   **Correct**

2 What causes Mr. Brooney's horse to wriggle his ears?

A He hears Sylvie sing a high note.

B He is bothered by a pesky fly.

C He is impatient waiting for Mr. Brooney.

D He is listening to Jane talking to him.

3 Read these sentences from the story. They tell Jane's thoughts about the horse.

He had wings and could carry her away.

He was the wooden horse of Troy and many men could step out of him.

He was a bridge that she could walk under.

Which of the following **best** describes what the reader learns about Jane's character based on her thoughts?

A She is fond of Mr. Brooney's horse.

B She wants to run away.

C She is very imaginative.

D She wishes she lived in another time.

4 Read the following table based on the story.

JANE'S ACTIONS

• She watches and watches Mr. Brooney's horse.
• She sits on the hitching post.
• She jumps off the post and marches over to the horse.
• _____

Which of these key details belongs on the blank line?

A She watches her brothers play on stilts.

B She helps her mother dust the parlor.

C She walks underneath the horse.

D She rides the horse down the street.

5 Which sentence is the **best** description of Mama's response to Jane's actions?

A Mama is too busy dusting the front parlor to notice what Jane is doing.

B Mama is very upset with Jane for walking under the horse.

C Mama does not see Jane because she is in the kitchen with Sylvie.

D Mama is proud of Jane for taking a risk and being so brave.

6 Which is the **best** summary of this story?

A Jane sees Mr. Brooney, the grocery man, drive his horse and wagon. She watches him deliver baskets of groceries to Mrs. Frost and other neighbors. While Mr. Brooney delivers groceries, his horse waits patiently for him to return. Jane spends a long time watching Mr. Brooney's horse.

B Jane and her brothers are outside playing. Soon, Mr. Brooney arrives in the neighborhood, driving his horse and wagon. While Mr. Brooney delivers groceries, Jane and her brothers pet the horse and feed him carrots. The horse flicks his long tail and stomps his feet.

C Jane sits outside on the hitching post watching Mr. Brooney's horse. Jane's mother is inside the house dusting the front parlor. Jane stays outside in order to avoid helping her mother with the spring cleaning. She also stays outside to avoid hearing Sylvie practice her graduation music.

D Jane sits on the hitching post and watches Mr. Brooney's horse. As Jane watches the horse, she imagines him as a bridge for her to walk under. Jane jumps off the hitching post and walks under the horse. Walking under the horse gives her a good feeling.

7 What details from the setting show that this story probably took place a long time ago? Describe two details about the setting that show this.

KEY DETAILS OF THE STORY'S SETTING

Detail 1:
Detail 2:

8 Describe what happens that gives Jane "an extraordinary feeling of satisfaction and elation" in the story. Why does Jane feel this way? Use details from the story to support your answer.

_____

_____

_____

_____

_____

_____

_____

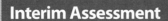

9   Answer Parts A, B, and C below.

Part A

Circle **one** word that describes Jane based on evidence from the text. There is more than one correct choice listed below.

dreamy	cautious	excited
naughty	cranky	thoughtful

Part B

Find a sentence in the passage with details that support your response to Part A. Write that sentence on the lines below.

_____

_____

_____

_____

Part C

Find a second sentence in the passage with details that support your response to Part A. Write that sentence on the lines below.

_____

_____

_____

_____

Performance Task—Extended Response

10 What lesson does Jane learn at the end of the story? How does her experience with the horse teach her this lesson? Be sure to include key details from the story in your answer.

In your answer, be sure to
- explain what Jane learns
- tell how the horse helps teach this lesson
- use key details from the story in your answer

Begin writing your answer below. Check your writing for correct spelling, grammar, capitalization, and punctuation.

_____

_____

_____

_____

_____

_____

_____

_____

_____

_____

_____

_____

_____

_____

_____

_____

_____

_____

_____

_____

_____

_____

_____

_____

_____

Unit 3
Craft and Structure in Informational Text

How are buildings like informational texts? Buildings have frameworks to hold them up. Similarly, informational texts have frameworks called **text structures**. The type of framework a building has depends on the type of building it is. Skyscrapers have frameworks of steel and concrete. Houses have frameworks mostly of wood. And, like a building, the structure a text has depends on what that text needs to do. Writers **craft** their texts to accomplish particular goals. Does a writer want to compare video games? Then the writer puts that information into a compare–contrast structure. Does a writer want to explain how volcanic eruptions create diamonds? Then the writer uses a cause–effect structure. A text structure is more than just organization—it is always organization with a purpose.

In this unit, you'll practice identifying unknown words. You'll describe text structures. And, you'll learn the differences between first- and secondhand accounts of events. So, put on your hard hat—or rather, your thinking cap—as we read all sorts of informational texts.

✓ Self Check

Before starting this unit, check off the skills you know below. As you complete each lesson, see how many more you can check off!

I know how to:	Before this unit	After this unit
find the meaning of unfamiliar words and phrases in an informational text.	☐	☐
describe cause–effect and compare–contrast text structures.	☐	☐
describe chronological and problem–solution text structures.	☐	☐
compare and contrast the differences between firsthand and secondhand accounts of the same topic.	☐	☐

Lesson 13   Part 1: Introduction

Unfamiliar Words

CCSS

RI.4.4: Determine the meaning of general academic and domain-specific words or phrases in a text relevant to a grade 4 topic or subject area.

Theme: *Science and Engineering*

Sometimes when you read, you may come across a word that is unfamiliar to you. As a reader, you can use your context clues to help you understand the word. **Context clues** are the words and sentences that surround the unfamiliar word.

Read the paragraph below, then do the activity that follows.

Inventing the Crane

Ancient Greek engineers thought of ways to make new machines from older ones. For example, they conceived of and built a compound machine called the crane. Their idea combined the lever, pulley, and wheel-and-axle into one machine.

In the paragraph, underline the phrase *conceived of*. Then circle possible context clues that will help you figure out what it means.

Conceived of is a phrase that you'll find in many kinds of texts. Read the table below to see how context clues can help you figure out the meaning of *conceived of*.

Complete the table by writing a definition of *conceived of* on the blank line.

Sentence Before	Sentence with Phrase	Sentence After
Ancient Greek engineers **thought of ways** to make new machines from older ones.	For example, they **conceived of** and built a compound machine called the crane.	Their **idea** combined the lever, pulley, and wheel-and-axle into one machine.

Meaning of phrase: *Conceived of* means _____

_____

When you come across a word or phrase you don't know, always look at the nearby sentences for clues. If you do this, you'll usually be able to figure out what the unknown word or phrase means.

Read these paragraphs from a science textbook.

Genre: **Science**

Fire and Air   *by Johanna Joyner*

Starting a fire is a bit like following a recipe. Getting anything **to combust** takes three ingredients: fuel, heat, and oxygen. All three are needed for burning to begin. But where do these ingredients come from? Fuel is anything that burns easily, including wood, paper, or grass. Heat can come from many places, but most people use matches. And oxygen is a gas in the air around us.

If a fire doesn't have enough of any one of the three ingredients, it will be weak. To strengthen the fire, just add one or more of the ingredients. It is simple to add more fuel or heat. But how do you add more oxygen? From a safe distance, blow on the fire. You will see it strengthen. Blowing adds oxygen to the fire, making it **vigorous**. Your fire will grow bigger, brighter, and stronger.

Explore how to answer this question: *"What are the meanings of* to combust *and* vigorous *as they are used in the text?"*

First, look for context clues in the text that tell what the phrase *to combust* means.

Sentence Before	Sentence with Phrase	Sentence After
_____ is a bit like following a recipe.	Getting anything **to combust** takes three ingredients: fuel, heat, and oxygen.	All three are needed for _____.
Meaning of phrase: *To combust* means _____.		

Now, look for context clues and use the table below to figure out what *vigorous* means.

Sentence Before	Sentence with Word	Sentence After
_____ _____	_____ _____	_____ _____
Meaning of phrase: *Vigorous* means _____.		

Read this experiment about fire. Use the Close Reading and the Hint to help you answer the question below.

Genre: **Experiment**

Close Reading

In this passage, **circle** the word *monitor*. Then **underline** phrases that give you clues about its meaning.

An Experiment with Fire   *by Allan Pomme*

What You Need

- MOST IMPORTANT: A TEACHER HELPING YOU
- three small candles (tealights)
- three saucers
- two glass jars, one larger than the other

What You Do

Put each candle on a saucer. Have your teacher light the candles. Put a jar over two of the candles. Pay attention to the candles. Monitor what happens over time. You will observe that the candle with the least air available is the first one extinguished. Keep watching to see which candle goes out next. Blow out the last candle.

Hint

In the original sentence, replace *monitor* with each answer choice. Which choice makes the most sense?

Circle the correct answer.

What does the word *monitor* mean as it is used in this passage?

A be careful of

B watch closely

C start on fire

D happen over time

✎ **Show Your Thinking**

Identify the context clues that helped you figure out the meaning of the word *monitor*.

_____

_____

 With a partner, determine the meaning of the word *extinguished* as it is used in the experiment. Discuss the context clues that helped you find the meaning.

Read the science passage, using the Study Buddy and the Close Reading to guide your reading.

This text has some words I don't know. I'll circle the words I'm not sure about. Then I'll read the text again, underlining any clues that help me figure out the word.

Close Reading

You might not know the word *renowned*. **Circle** that word. Then **underline** clues that help tell its meaning.

Paragraph 3 has the word *subterranean*. What does it mean? **Underline** any words that give clues to what *subterranean* means.

Genre: **Science**

Over Bridge, Under Tunnel   *by Lloyd Frank*

1   Mountains, lakes, and rivers can get in the way of people traveling from one place to another. There are structures that help people pass such obstacles. Bridges and tunnels help people overcome such barriers.

2   Bridges and tunnels are different in design and placement. A bridge is built over a body of water, a highway, or a railroad track. A tunnel, in contrast, is a passageway under the ground, under a body of water, or through a mountain. Bridges vary in shape and are often placed above ground or water. Some are even famous. The Golden Gate Bridge is one of the most renowned bridges in the world. This celebrated structure crosses over the entrance to San Francisco Bay and connects San Francisco to northern California. The Golden Gate is known for its length and height. But it is best known for its beauty. People come from all over the world not just to cross the Golden Gate but simply to look at it.

3   Of course, not even the world's most famous tunnel gets many visitors who just want to look. It's hard to get a good view of a subterranean passage. But since the Channel Tunnel opened in 1994, it has transported millions of people. The Channel Tunnel, or "Chunnel," runs beneath the English Channel and connects France and England. The Chunnel is a rail tunnel. The only automobiles that cross it are carried on special railway cars. The Chunnel is not the longest tunnel in the world, but it is one of the few tunnels that connect two countries.

Hints

How might a mountain, lake, or river affect how people travel?

Use the Hints on this page to help you answer the questions.

1 Read this sentence from paragraph 1 of the text.

> There are structures that help people pass such obstacles.

What is the meaning of *obstacles* as it is used in the text?

A Things made below or above ground.

B Things that slow or stop movement.

C Things that help people travel.

D Things built through mountains or over water.

People from all over the world come to look at the Golden Gate Bridge.

2 Paragraph 2 says, "The Golden Gate Bridge is one of the most renowned bridges in the world." What is the meaning of *renowned* as it is used in the text?

A strongest

B long-lasting

C beautiful

D well-known

The root *terra* comes from a Latin word for "earth." What does the prefix *sub-* mean?

3 Read this sentence from paragraph 3 of the text.

> It's hard to get a good view of a subterranean passage.

In your own words, write a definition of the word *subterranean*. Then list two words or phrases that helped you define the word.

_____

_____

_____

_____

_____

_____

_____

Read the science passage. Then answer the questions that follow.

Seashells

by Bela Moté

1   If you walk along the seashore, you will probably see many kinds of shells. Seashells were once the homes of live animals. The animals that live inside shells have soft bodies, so they need their shells to protect them from harm. Their shells save them from storms or predators such as starfish, birds, and otters. Shells also give the animals a shape. In that way, shells are like skeletons on the outside of the body. When the animals die, the shells remain.

2   Creatures with shells belong to a group of animals called **mollusks**. Not all mollusks have shells. Of the mollusks that do have shells, there are two main groups.

Univalves

3   More than three-quarters of all mollusks are **univalves**, a word that means "having a shell that is all one piece." The shell is coiled, and inside the coil is the soft body of the mollusk. Many univalves are named for their appearance. Look at the examples below. Does the helmet shell remind you of a helmet? How about the worm and slipper shells?

Helmet Shell

Worm Shell

Slipper Shell

4   Some univalves have small holes in their shells. Abalone shells have a series of holes. Water and wastes are expelled, or pushed out, through the holes. The inside of an abalone shell gleams with different rainbow colors. This iridescent substance is called mother-of-pearl.

Abalone Shell

Bivalves

5   After univalves, **bivalves** are the next largest group of mollusks. When a bivalve is alive, the two parts of its shell are hinged. After the animal dies, you may find just one part of the shell lying on the beach.

6   Many bivalves have names that reflect their appearance. A jackknife is a knife that folds into its own case. The jackknife clam has an appropriate name because it has about the same shape as a closed jackknife. Are angel wing and kitten's paw fitting names for the shells shown here?

Jackknife Shell   Angel Wing Shell   Kitten's Paw Shell

7   There are many different kinds of clams, from very small to very large. The giant clam is the largest bivalve. Some are four feet long and weigh 500 pounds. The giant clam even grows its own food. Tiny plants get caught in the clam. The plants get what they need from the clam, but eventually the clam eats the plants.

Giant Clam Shell

8   Another common bivalve is the oyster. All oysters can make pearls, but the pearl oyster makes the most beautiful ones. A pearl is an accident. A grain of sand or something else gets inside the oyster shell. An oyster is creating new shell material all the time. To protect itself from the foreign body, the oyster covers it with the same material that the oyster's shell is made of. The result is a pearl.

Pearl Oyster Shell

Answer Form

1 Ⓐ Ⓑ Ⓒ Ⓓ
2 Ⓐ Ⓑ Ⓒ Ⓓ   **Number**
3 Ⓐ Ⓑ Ⓒ Ⓓ   **Correct** /3

1   **What is the meaning of the word "predators" as it is used in paragraph 1?**

A   Animals that are larger than other animals.

B   Animals that live near or in the sea.

C   Animals that have skeletons inside their bodies.

D   Animals that hunt other animals for food.

2   Read the following sentence from paragraph 4 of the passage.

　　This iridescent substance is called mother-of-pearl.

What words from the passage can help you figure out the meaning of "iridescent"?

A "inside of an abalone shell"

B "gleams with different rainbow colors"

C "the two parts of its shell are hinged"

D "the next largest group of mollusks"

3   Read the following sentences from paragraph 5 of the passage.

　　When a bivalve is alive, the two parts of its shell are hinged. After the animal dies, you may find just one part of the shell lying on the beach.

What is the meaning of "bivalve" as it is used in the passage?

A having a shell that is all one piece

B having a shell with two pieces

C having a hard outer shell

D having a soft outer shell

4   Paragraph 6 states, "The jackknife clam has an appropriate name because it has about the same shape as a closed jackknife." Explain what the word *appropriate* mean as it is used in the passage. Support your definition with **one** context clue from the passage.

_____

_____

_____

_____

 **Self Check** *Go back and see what you can check off on the Self Check on page 117.*

Text Structures, Part 1: Cause–Effect and Compare–Contrast

CCSS

RI.4.5: Describe the overall structure (e.g., . . . comparison, cause/effect . . .) of events, ideas, concepts, or information in a text or part of a text.

Theme: *Entertainment History*

A text with a **cause–effect** structure connects what happens (**effects**) to what makes them happen (**causes**). Such texts use words like *because, therefore, so,* and *as a result.*

Read the paragraph below. Circle any signal words that indicate its text structure.

> The earliest sound recordings were made on tin foil. Because the foil ripped easily and sounded bad, inventors looked for better materials. Later recordings were therefore put on harder metal or wax, which lasted longer and sounded better.

The diagram below shows how one cause stated in the paragraph produced an effect.

Cause	Effect
Foil recordings ripped easily and sounded bad.	Inventors looked for better materials and put later recordings on harder metal or wax.

A text can also **compare and contrast** how events, ideas, and concepts are similar or different. Such texts use words such as *both, alike, unlike, similar, different,* and others.

Read the paragraph below. Circle any signal words that indicate its text structure.

> Thomas Edison invented the phonograph in 1877. It played sound when the listener spun a hand crank that turned a metal tube. In 1886, Alexander Bell invented the graphophone. Like the phonograph, the graphophone played sound and was powered by the listener. Unlike the phonograph, the graphophone was operated by means of a foot pedal that turned a wax-covered tube.

The table below lists the similarities and the differences of the two machines.

Just the Phonograph	Both Machines	Just the Graphophone
• Invented by Edison in 1877 • Operated by hand crank • Recordings on metal tube	• Invented in 1800s • Powered by listeners • Played sound recordings	• Invented by Bell in 1886 • Operated by foot pedal • Recordings on wax tube

Understanding the **structure** of a text helps you understand how the writer is connecting one or more events, ideas, or concepts with each other.

Read the first two paragraphs of a feature article about a famous event in the history of radio.

Genre: **Feature Article**

The Night the Martians Landed   *by Scott Carey*

October 30, 1938, was perhaps the most frightening night that thousands of Americans would ever experience. It was the night that the science fiction novel *The War of the Worlds* was presented in the form of a radio news broadcast.

Orson Welles, a famous movie actor and director, made the broadcast from a studio in New York City. The story was about Martians invading the Earth. Before the program began, Welles explained that the "news broadcast" was fiction. But many listeners tuned in late. Therefore, they missed Welles's explanation that this was a radio play. As a result, thousands of people thought that the Earth was really being invaded by Martians!

(continued)

Explore how to answer this question: *"What text structure organizes the information in the second paragraph?"*

First, try to figure out how the paragraph connects the information it provides.

- The second paragraph tells what made two events happen. It tells about a cause.

- The second paragraph also tells what those events were. It tells about two _____.

So, the second paragraph organizes information in a _____ text structure.

Next, look for phrases in the second paragraph common to the text structure you just identified.

- Two phrases common to a cause–effect structure are _____.

Complete the diagram below. Use details from the second paragraph to complete it.

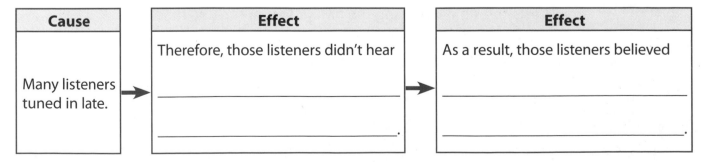

Cause	Effect	Effect
Many listeners tuned in late.	Therefore, those listeners didn't hear _____ _____ .	As a result, those listeners believed _____ _____ .

Close Reading

A compare–contrast structure uses words such as *both*, *alike*, *unlike*, *similar*, and *different*. **Circle** these words if you find them.

Continue reading the article about the "The War of the Worlds" radio broadcast. Use the Close Reading and the Hint to help you answer the question below.

(continued from page 128)

As people listened, they began to panic because the broadcast seemed so real. Some people called their friends and relatives to warn them. Others alerted local police stations to the danger. Still others ran out into the streets, into parks, and into their cars, hoping to escape the "invasion." Traffic jams were everywhere, and telephone lines were overloaded. It was a terrifying night for both citizens and police alike.

The next day, the newspapers told of the "fake" news broadcast. Thousands of people had heard and believed it— but none of it was true. Those who lived through it have never forgotten it.

Hint

Look for the choice with words that signal a comparison structure.

Circle the correct answer.

Which sentence from the article makes a comparison?

A "Orson Welles, a famous movie actor and director, made the broadcast from a studio in New York City."

B "Before the program began, Welles explained that the 'news broadcast' was fiction."

C "As people listened, they began to panic because the broadcast seemed so real."

D "It was a terrifying night for both citizens and police alike."

✎ | **Show Your Thinking**

 Look at the answer that you chose above. Discuss with a partner why you chose that answer.

Read the feature article, using the Study Buddy and the Close Reading to guide your reading.

This text is about two TV cartoons. What text structure would a writer find most useful for telling about two similar things?

Close Reading

Look for and **underline** comparison words such as *like*, *both*, *similar*, and *different*.

Paragraph 3 describes some causes and their effects. **Write** a "C" next to each sentence that tells about a cause. Then **write** an "E" next to each sentence that describes an effect.

Genre: **Feature Article**

Cartoons for Grown-Ups   *by Jacob Miller*

1   On September 29, 1959, the American Broadcasting System (ABC) aired the first cartoon on prime-time television. *Rocky and His Friends* starred a playful flying squirrel named Rocky and his sidekick, Bullwinkle the Moose. These talking animals lived in the present-day (and imaginary) small town of Frostbite Falls, Minnesota. The squirrel and moose faced tense situations caused by two mischievous Russian agents, Boris Badenov and Natasha Fatale. Their adventures created many amusing stories. This cartoon, later called *The Bullwinkle Show*, inspired a feature film, comic books, and generations of fans.

2   A year later, another prime-time cartoon premiered on ABC: *The Flintstones*. Unlike *The Bullwinkle Show*, *The Flintstones* main stars were humans. Fred and Wilma Flintstone and their neighbors Barney and Betty Rubble lived in the town of Bedrock. Much of the cartoon's humor stemmed from the characters' use of modern technology in a prehistoric setting. Like *The Bullwinkle Show*, *The Flintstones* also inspired films, comics, and fans.

3   Despite their differences, *The Bullwinkle Show* and *The Flintstones* followed similar recipes for success. Both shows had clever dialogue and interesting characters. They were simple enough for young children but sophisticated enough to hold the attention of adults. Those reasons are why these cartoons succeeded in the 1960s. It's also why cartoons such as *The Simpsons* appeal to both adults and children today.

Hints

Are the two television shows entirely similar?

Use the Hints on this page to help you answer the questions.

1 Paragraph 1 tells about *The Bullwinkle Show*. Paragraph 2 describes *The Flintstones*. What else does paragraph 2 do?

A It explains how *The Bullwinkle Show* caused the ABC network to start airing *The Flintstones*.

B It describes some similarities and differences between *The Bullwinkle Show* and *The Flintstones*.

C It tells how drawing humans in *The Flintstones* solved problems caused by drawing animals in *The Bullwinkle Show*.

D It lists the events that led Fred and Wilma Flintstone to meet Barney and Betty Rubble.

The question asks about the text's main structure. How is *most* of the text organized?

2 Which of the following best describes the main text structure of the entire article "Cartoons for Grown-Ups"?

A It has a comparison structure because it tells how *The Bullwinkle Show* and *The Flintstones* are alike and unlike.

B It has a cause–effect structure because it explains how *Rocky and His Friends* led viewers to enjoy *The Simpsons*.

C It has a comparison structure because it tells how *Rocky and His Friends* differed from *The Bullwinkle Show*.

D It has a cause–effect structure because it explains why ABC started showing cartoons in 1959 and 1960.

Sometimes it's easiest to first find an effect, then try to figure out its cause.

3 The cause–effect diagram below lists one cause and one effect described in paragraph 3. Complete the diagram by writing one more cause and one more effect described in paragraph 3.

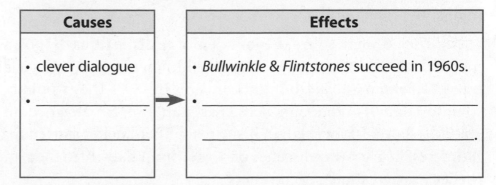

Causes	Effects
• clever dialogue	• *Bullwinkle & Flintstones* succeed in 1960s.
• _____	• _____
_____	_____.

Read the passage from a book about the history of movies. Then answer the questions that follow.

from *The History of Movie Making*
by Gallimard Jeunesse

1   Lights! Action . . . but no camera. Centuries before Hollywood existed, people used light and screens to create moving images. In the 18th and 19th centuries, magic lanterns were popular in Europe. The earliest had a simple lens and used candles to light up pictures painted on glass slides.

2   In 1885, George Eastman of Rochester, New York, introduced paper-backed film. Thomas Alva Edison and his assistant, W. K. L. Dickson, used George Eastman's flexible film when they made a motion picture camera. Their Kinetograph, patented in 1891, had a sprocket, or wheel with teeth. An electric motor turned the sprocket. The sprocket teeth hooked the perforations and pulled the film through the camera.

The First Picture Show

3   Paris, 1894: Louis Lumière peeps into an Edison Kinetoscope projecting machine. He's inspired! Paris 1895: Louis and his brother Auguste Lumière project the first publicly screened film, using their own invention, the *Cinématographe*. It combined the strong lamp and lens of a magic lantern with a shutter-and-film reel mechanism. By 1898, the Lumières had collected almost 1,000 short films. Most of them were real-life footage or news events from around the world. But Georges Méliès, a Parisian theater magician, had some fantastic ideas that would take film beyond reality.

4   The Lumière brothers' hand-cranked invention (1895) was a combination of camera, projector, and printer. The camera could shoot film. The projector kept the film still, while a frame (image) was projected on screen; then the frame was quickly advanced. Some audiences were shocked by the realistic pictures. The train moved as if it would plunge right into the audience. Supposedly, some frightened viewers ran out of the theater!

Méliès the Magician

5   The Lumières were the founders of realistic films. It took a magician to create a whole new type of film. Georges Méliès, a well-known Parisian magician and theater owner, tried to buy a *Cinématographe* from the Lumières in 1895. They would not sell it to him. So Méliès went to London and bought some Eastman film. He designed his own camera and built a studio, a 25 x 55-foot shed, in his garden. Then Méliès started making films. At first like the Lumières, he shot travel scenes or scenes from daily life. Then, quite by accident, Georges Méliès learned about special effects.

Hocus-Pocus

6   In 1896, Méliès' camera jammed while he was filming a Paris street. It took him a few seconds to fix it and continue shooting. Meanwhile, the street scene changed: A bus drove away and a hearse drove up. When Méliès projected his film, he was astonished to see the bus suddenly turn into a hearse! He began to experiment with this kind of stop-motion photography.

A Trip to the Moon

7   In 1902, Méliès produced the science-fiction classic *A Trip to the Moon*, which brought him worldwide fame. The approximately 11-minute silent film was based on the work of Jules Verne. It showed the adventures of six astronomers who pile into a rocket, get shot out of a cannon, and land smack in the eye of the man in the moon. Méliès' Star Film studio used extraordinary sets, props, and film effects to do things like make the moon's face move.

1   The sentences below are from paragraph 5 of the passage.

> At first like the Lumières, he shot travel scenes or scenes from daily life. Then, quite by accident, Georges Méliès learned about special effects.

Which of the following **best** describes the text structure of these sentences?

A   Cause–effect: The sentences tell how the Lumières' films showed Méliès how to make special effects.

B   Comparison: The sentences tell how Méliès' films were similar to and different from the Lumières' films.

C   Cause–effect: The sentences tell how Méliès' films led the Lumières to film scenes of daily life.

D   Comparison: The sentences tell how the Lumiéres' films and Méliès' films had nothing in common.

2 Which sentence from the passage describes a cause and its effect?

    A "In the 18th and 19th centuries, magic lanterns were popular in Europe."

    B "In 1885, George Eastman of Rochester, New York, introduced paper-backed film."

    C "The Lumière brothers' hand-cranked invention (1895) was a combination of camera, projector, and printer."

    D "In 1902, Méliès produced the science-fiction classic *A Trip to the Moon*, which brought him worldwide fame."

3 The sentences below are from paragraph 5 of the passage.

> Georges Méliès, a well-known Parisian magician and theater owner, tried to buy a *Cinématographe* from the Lumières in 1895. They would not sell it to him. So Méliès went to London and bought some Eastman film.

Describe the text structure in these sentences of the passage. Support your answer with at least **two** details from the sentences.

_____

_____

_____

_____

_____

_____

_____

_____

 **Self Check**   *Go back and see what you can check off on the Self Check on page 117.*

Text Structures, Part 2: Chronology and Problem–Solution

CCSS

RI.4.5: Describe the overall structure (e.g., chronology . . . problem/solution) of events, ideas, concepts, or information in a text or part of a text.

Theme: *Real-Life Adventures*

A **chronological** text structure tells about events in the order they occur. Signal words such as *before*, *then*, *during*, and *finally* tell you a text is organized by chronology. Other words that signal chronology include *first*, *second*, *next*, *later*, *after*, and *thereafter*.

Read the paragraph below. Circle signal words that indicate its text structure.

> I'll never forget the storm last October. Before the storm started, I found some blankets and flashlights. During the storm, I played games with my family. Finally, I turned on the radio and listened to the local weather report. *Crack!*

A **problem–solution** text structure tells about a problem and how it can be solved. Look for signal words such as *problem*, *solution*, *challenge*, *fixed*, *issue*, and *resolved*.

Read the paragraph below. Circle signal words that indicate its text structure.

> The ground shook as a tree in our front yard toppled over, falling across power lines and cutting off our electricity. We faced the challenge of getting through the night without lights or heat. We resolved the first issue with flashlights and candles. Dad fixed the second problem by making a fire in the fireplace.

Below, summarize one problem and its solution as identified in the passage.

Problem	Solution

Learning how writers put together their ideas helps you follow along and find information quickly. You can also try using similar structures in your own writing.

Read the start of a memoir about a man who takes care of an injured wild animal.

Genre: **Memoir**

Treating the Red Fox　　*by Mark B. Champlin*

I first spotted the red fox on a June morning. It was beside the tool shed, trembling. I approached the animal cautiously and saw its left hind leg was injured. I went inside my cabin and got my medical bag. Then, with caution, I returned to the fox. Next, I gently lifted its injured leg and decided to attach a splint. The fox settled back and let me proceed with my work. On my porch, I set up a wooden box padded with pillows so the fox could heal. Beside the box I placed bowls of food and water that I refilled daily.

One morning in July, I stepped out to the porch and saw that the red fox was gone. I checked the porch each day after, but the fox was nowhere to be found.

(continued)

Explore how to answer this question: *"What is the text structure of the first paragraph?"*

Reread the first paragraph. Circle any signal words that tell you how this text is organized. Look back at the two lists of signal words on page 135 to help you.

Now complete this diagram with details from the first paragraph.

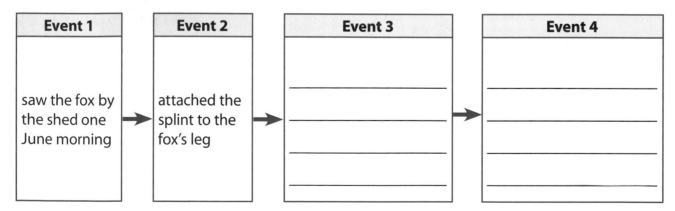

Event 1	Event 2	Event 3	Event 4
saw the fox by the shed one June morning	attached the splint to the fox's leg		

Describe the text structure of the first paragraph. Use details from the text in your answer.

_____

_____

_____

Continue reading about the red fox. Use the Close Reading and the Hint to help you answer the question below.

Close Reading

Circle any words that signal a text structure.

(continued from page 136)

    Late one August afternoon, I spied the red fox coming up the path to my cabin. A short distance behind, a silver fox was limping along. I watched as the animals approached the tool shed. The silver fox was fearful, but the red fox apparently resolved the issue by assuring it the area was safe. The silver fox settled down beside the tool shed. The red fox observed its friend for a few moments, then returned to the dense woods. As I had done once before, I entered the cabin, located my medical bag, and returned outside to treat the silver fox.

Hint

Look at the list of problem–solution signal words on page 135.

Circle the correct answer.

Which sentence from the passage has a problem–solution structure?

A "Late one August afternoon, I spied the red fox coming up the path to my cabin."

B "The silver fox was fearful, but the red fox apparently resolved the issue by assuring it the area was safe."

C "The red fox observed its friend for a few moments, then returned to the dense woods."

D "As I had done once before, I entered the cabin, located my medical bag, and returned outside to treat the silver fox."

✎ Show Your Thinking

Look at the answers that you did not choose. What text structure do those sentences have?

_____

_____

 With a partner, describe one important difference between a chronological text structure and a problem–solution text structure.

Read the history passage, using the Study Buddy and Close Reading to guide your reading.

Figuring out a text's structure helps me understand it. As I read, I'll look for how the writer put her ideas together.

Close Reading

Do paragraphs 1 and 2 tell about problems, or do they tell a series of events? **Circle** words that help you figure this out.

Paragraphs 3 and 4 describe a problem and its solution. **Underline** both the problem and the solution.

Genre: **History**

30 Seconds of Fuel   *by Theresa Baker*

1   In July 1969, three astronauts blasted off for the Moon. Their goal was not only to land on the Moon but also to walk on its surface. The journey from Earth to Moon was quiet, and the astronauts were patient and calm during the trip. The landing, however, would be quite exciting.

2   After getting near the Moon, the landing ship, named *Eagle*, separated from the command ship. The command ship then remained in orbit around the Moon. During the landing ship's descent to the Moon, the astronaut flying the ship made an announcement. Astronaut Neil Armstrong said, "The *Eagle* has wings." He meant that the landing ship was flying well and doing its job.

3   As the *Eagle* began its final approach, alarms sounded. By now, fuel was running low. Looking out the window, Armstrong realized the terrain was not good for landing. The problem was that it was rocky and dangerous. The landing site was supposed to be smooth.

4   There was less than a minute of fuel left for a landing. If they ran out, the *Eagle* would be forced to cancel its flight and go back to the command ship. Armstrong had to decide how to meet this challenge. Should he call off the landing? Or should he look for another landing spot? He quickly chose to fly the ship to another area. Just seconds later, the ship landed in an area of the Moon called the Sea of Tranquility. There were only about 30 seconds of fuel left. Armstrong announced, "The *Eagle* has landed."

Hints

The astronauts' flight from Earth to the Moon was uneventful. Nothing happened that needed fixing.

Use the Hints on this page to help you answer the questions.

1 Which of the following best describes the text structure used to connect the events told about in paragraphs 1 and 2?

　A Chronological: Paragraphs 1 and 2 tell what happened between the launch and the *Eagle*'s approach to the Moon.

　B Problem–solution: Paragraphs 1 and 2 tell what troubles the astronauts had during the flight and how they solved them.

　C Chronological: Paragraphs 1 and 2 tell how the astronauts landed on the Moon and went for a walk afterward.

　D Problem–solution: Paragraphs 1 and 2 tell how the *Eagle* was able to separate from the command ship in order to land.

Typically, in a problem–solution structure, the writer describes the problem first, then describes one or more possible solutions.

2 Paragraphs 3 and 4 describe a problem that Neil Armstrong faced. Those paragraphs also describe the solution he reached.

Describe the problem: _____

_____

Describe the solution: _____

_____

_____

Signal words are evidence that the author is using a problem–solution text structure.

3 Describe the evidence you see of the author using a problem–solution text structure in paragraphs 3 and 4 of this passage. Use at least three words or phrases from the passage to support your answer.

_____

_____

_____

_____

_____

_____

Read this memoir. Then answer the questions that follow.

Tenzing Norgay, along with Sir Edmund Hillary, was one of the first two people to reach the summit of Mount Everest on May 29th, 1953. The following passage is taken from his autobiography.

from *Tiger of the Snows: The Autobiography of Tenzing of Everest*

by Tenzing Norgay

1   On top of the rock cliff we rested again. Certainly, after the climb up the gap we were both a bit breathless, but after some slow pulls at the oxygen I am feeling fine. I look up; the top is very close now; and my hearts thumps with excitement and joy. Then we are on our way again. Climbing again . . . .

2   Then the rocks, too, are beneath us. We are back among the snowy humps. They are curving off to the right, and each time we pass one I wonder, "Is the next the last one? Is the next the last?" Finally we reach a place where we can see past the humps, and beyond them is the great open sky and brown plains. We are looking down the far side of the mountain upon Tibet. Ahead of us now is only one more hump—the last hump. It is not a pinnacle. The way to it is an easy snow slope, wide enough for two men to go side by side. About thirty feet away we stop for a minute and look up. Then we go on . . . .

3   A little below the summit Hillary and I stopped. We looked up. Then we went on. The rope that joined us was thirty feet long, but I held most of it in loops in my hand, so that there was only about six feet between us . . . .

4   We stepped up. We were there. The dream had come true . . . .

5   What we did first was what all climbers do when they reach the top of their mountain. We shook hands. But this was not enough for Everest. I waved my arms in the air and then threw them around Hillary, and we thumped each other on the back until, even with the oxygen, we were almost breathless. Then we looked around. It was eleven-thirty in the morning, the sun was shining, and the sky was the deepest blue I have ever seen. Only a gentle breeze was blowing, coming from the direction of Tibet, and the plume of snow that always blows from Everest's summit was very small . . . .

6   It was such a sight as I had never seen before and would never see again: wild, wonderful, and terrible. But terror was not what I felt. I loved the mountains too well for that. I loved Everest too well. At that great moment for which I had waited all my life my mountain did not seem to me a lifeless thing of rock and ice, but warm and friendly and living. She was a mother hen, and the other mountains were chicks under her wings. I too, I felt, had only to spread my own wings to cover and shelter the brood that I loved.

Answer Form

1 Ⓐ Ⓑ Ⓒ Ⓓ

2 Ⓐ Ⓑ Ⓒ Ⓓ   **Number**

3 Ⓐ Ⓑ Ⓒ Ⓓ   **Correct** /3

1   Which sentence from the passage tells of a problem and its solution?

   A "Certainly, after the climb up the gap we were both a bit breathless, but after some slow pulls at the oxygen I am feeling fine."

   B "The way to it is an easy snow slope, wide enough for two men to go side by side."

   C "I waved my arms in the air and then threw them around Hillary, and we thumped each other on the back until, even with the oxygen, we were almost breathless."

   D "It was such a sight as I had never seen before and would never see again: wild, wonderful, and terrible."

2   Which of the following **best** describes the text structure of paragraph 2?

   A Problem–solution: Paragraph 2 explains how Tenzing and Hillary solved the problem of moving among the snowy humps.

   B Chronological: Paragraph 2 tells how Tenzing and Hillary passed the snowy humps and reached the snow slope.

   C Problem–solution: Paragraph 2 explains how Tenzing and Hillary overcame the snow slope to reach the pinnacle.

   D Chronological: Paragraph 2 tells how many minutes passed between walking past the first snowy hump and reaching the snow slope.

3   The sentences below are from *Tiger of the Snows*.

   We went on slowly, steadily. And _____ we were there. Hillary
   stepped on top _____. And I stepped up after him. . . .

   Which words **most likely** go in the two blanks?

   A   then, first

   B   before, last

   C   while, before

   D   next, during

4   Part of paragraph 5 is shown below.

   What we did first was what all climbers do when they reach the top of their
   mountain. We shook hands. But this was not enough for Everest. I waved my
   arms in the air and then threw them around Hillary, and we thumped each
   other on the back until, even with the oxygen, we were almost breathless.
   Then we looked around. It was eleven-thirty in the morning,
   the sun was shining, and the sky was the deepest blue I have ever seen.

   Describe the text structure the writer uses to organize this information.
   Use at least **three** specific details from the text to support your answer.

   _____

   _____

   _____

   _____

   _____

✓ **Self Check**   *Go back and see what you can check off on the Self Check on page 117.*

Lesson 16   Part 1: Introduction 👥

Comparing Accounts of the Same Topic

CCSS

RI.4.6: Compare and contrast a firsthand and secondhand account of the same event or topic; describe the differences in focus and the information provided.

Theme: *History in the Making*

What is the difference between a firsthand account and a secondhand account? Let's think about the differences by using an example. In 1900, a powerful hurricane wrecked the city of Galveston, Texas. It took many years for the city to recover.

Circle the character who was in Galveston during the hurricane of 1900.

The boy was in Galveston during the hurricane. His description of what he experienced would be a **firsthand account**. The girl was not in Galveston, but she knows about the hurricane from what others tell her. Her description would be a **secondhand account**.

When you read different accounts of the same topic, you can compare what each account **focuses** on. This means you can compare what the writers pay attention to. You can also compare the **information**, or facts, each writer chooses to give.

Imagine that the boy and the girl write down their thoughts about the hurricane.

Based on details in the cartoon, what do you think the boy's account would focus on?

_____

Based on details in the cartoon, what do you think the girl's account would focus on?

_____

Reading and comparing firsthand and secondhand accounts of the same event or topic can give you a rich picture of what happened and why. It can bring history alive.

Read the first two paragraphs from this newspaper article about the sinking of the *Titanic*.

Genre: **News Article**

Titanic Sinks Four Hours After Hitting Iceberg

from *The New York Times*, April 16, 1912

The first news of the disaster to the *Titanic* was received by the Marconi wireless station[1] here at 10:25 o'clock last night . . . . The *Titanic* was first heard giving the distress signal "C.Q.D.," which was answered by a number of ships, including the *Carpathia*, the *Baltic*, and the *Olympic*. The *Titanic* said she had struck an iceberg and was in immediate need of assistance.

At 10:55 o'clock the *Titanic* reported she was sinking by the head, and at 11:25 o'clock the station here established communication with the Allan liner *Virginian*, from Halifax for Liverpool, and notified her of the *Titanic*'s urgent need of assistance and gave her the *Titanic*'s position. . . .

[1] **Marconi wireless station:** radio station

(continued)

Explore how to answer this question: *"Is this article a firsthand or a secondhand account?"*

First, ask yourself: What would a firsthand account of the sinking of the *Titanic* be like? And how would a firsthand account differ from a secondhand account?

A firsthand account would be written by a person who was on the *Titanic* when the iceberg struck it. The writer would have experienced the events—and lived to tell the tale.

In contrast, a secondhand account would be written by a person who _____

_____

_____

Now reread the paragraphs. Where did the writer get the information about the *Titanic* from?

_____

Based on the details in the text, the news article is a _____ account.

Continue reading the news article about the *Titanic*. Use the Close Reading and the Hint to help you answer the question below.

Close Reading

Find and **underline** details that help you understand the wireless operator's role as the *Titanic* sank.

(continued from page 144)

At 11:36 o'clock the *Titanic* informed the *Olympic* that they were putting the women off in boats and instructed the *Olympic* to have her boats ready to transfer the passengers.

The *Titanic*, during all this time, continued to give distress signals and to announce her position. The wireless operator seemed absolutely cool and clear-headed, his sending throughout being steady and perfectly formed, and the judgment used by him was of the best.

The last signals heard from the *Titanic* were received at 12:27 A.M., when the *Virginian* reported having heard a few blurred signals which ended abruptly.

Hint

Think about what the wireless operator did on the *Titanic*. How would his view of this event differ from the news reporter's view?

Circle the correct answer.

Suppose the wireless operator wrote about the sinking of the *Titanic*. How would his account most likely be different than the account given by the newspaper article?

A His account would describe what he saw, felt, and did.

B His account would focus on another person's experience.

C His account would report facts but no personal observations.

D His account would tell about how to operate the wireless radio.

✎ Show Your Thinking

 Imagine that a news reporter on the *Titanic* writes about that experience. Discuss how that reporter's account would be similar to and different from the article you just read. Identify whether this account would be firsthand or secondhand.

Read the memoir, using the Study Buddy and Close Reading to guide your reading.

Genre: **Memoir**

I know that a memoir is usually a firsthand account of what the writer saw, felt, thought, and did. In other words, the writer will probably tell what he experienced.

Close Reading

In the memoir, **underline** four sentences with facts about the sinking not told in the newspaper article.

The article expresses almost no emotion. This memoir is quite different. **Circle** words and phrases that express how the writer feels about his experience.

"The Sinking of the *Titanic*"
by James McGough, in Sinking of the *Titanic* and Great Sea Disasters

1   As the life-boats pulled away the officers ordered the bands to play, and their music did much to quell panic. It was a heart-breaking sight . . . to see the great ship go down. First she listed to the starboard, on which side the collision had occurred, then she settled slowly but steadily, without hope of remaining afloat.

2   The *Titanic* was all aglow with lights as if for a function. First we saw the lights of the lower deck snuffed out. A while later and the second deck illumination was extinguished in a similar manner. Then the third and upper decks were darkened, and without plunging or rocking the great ship disappeared slowly from the surface of the sea . . . .

3   The sea was calm—calm as the water in a tumbler. But it was freezing cold. None had dressed heavily, and all, therefore, suffered intensely. The women did not shriek or grow hysterical while we waited through the awful night for help. We men stood at the oars, stood because there was no room for us to sit, and kept the boat headed into the swell to prevent her capsizing. Another boat was at our side, but all the others were scattered around the water.

4   Finally, shortly before 6 o'clock, we saw the lights of the *Carpathia* approaching. Gradually she picked up the survivors in the other boats and then approached us.

Hints

A memoir is one type of firsthand account.

Use the Hints on this page to help you answer the questions.

1 The facts in the news article on pages 144 and 145 came from radio reports. In the memoir on page 146, where did James McGough get his facts from?

   A He read about the events in the newspaper article.

   B He heard about the events from friends on the ship.

   C He imagined the events and wrote a story about them.

   D He experienced the events as they happened.

Compare the information in each answer choice with the information given in both passages.

2 Which information did McGough give that was not in the article?

   A The *Olympic* traveled to the *Titanic*'s location.

   B Passengers were put into lifeboats.

   C The lights on the *Titanic* went out deck by deck.

   D The *Titanic* was struck by an iceberg.

The sentences describe the same event. How they describe it is quite different. Look at the words the writers use. Think about how the writers want their readers to respond to their words.

3 The table below has sentences from the article and the memoir.

Newspaper Article	Memoir
At 11:36 o'clock the *Titanic* informed the *Olympic* that they were putting the women off in boats	As the life-boats pulled away the officers ordered the bands to play, and their music did much to quell panic.

Describe one way these accounts are alike. Then tell one way in which they differ. Use two details from the sentences in your answer.

_____

_____

_____

_____

_____

_____

_____

Read the memoir and the newspaper article. Then answer the questions that follow.

from *To Space and Back*

by Sally Ride

Launch minus 10 seconds . . . 9 . . . 8 . . . 7 . . . The three launch engines light. The shuttle shakes and strains at the bolts holding it to the launch pad. The computers check the engines. It isn't up to us anymore—the computers will decide whether we launch.

3 . . . 2 . . . 1 . . . The rockets light! The shuttle leaps off the launch pad in a cloud of steam and a trail of fire. Inside, the ride is rough and loud. Our heads are rattling around inside our helmets. We can barely hear the voices from Mission Control in our headsets above the thunder of the rockets and engines. For an instant I wonder if everything is working right. But there's no time to wonder, and no time to be scared.

In only a few seconds we zoom past the clouds. Two minutes later the rockets burn out, and with a brilliant whitish-orange flash, they fall away from the shuttle as it streaks on toward space. Suddenly the ride becomes very, very smooth and quiet. The shuttle is still attached to the big tank, and the launch engines are pushing us out of Earth's atmosphere. The sky is black. All we can see of the trail of fire behind us is a faint, pulsating glow through the top window.

Launch plus six minutes. The force pushing us against the backs of our seats steadily increases. We can barely move because we're being held in place by a force of 3 g's—three times the force of gravity we feel on Earth. At first we don't mind it—we've all felt much more than that when we've done acrobatics in our jet training airplanes. But that lasted only a few seconds, and this seems to go on forever. After a couple of minutes of 3 g's, we're uncomfortable, straining to hold our books on our laps and craning our necks against the force to read the instruments. I find myself wishing we'd hurry up and get into orbit.

Launch plus eight and one-half minutes. The launch engines cut off. Suddenly, the force is gone, and we lurch forward in our seats. During the next few minutes the empty fuel tank drops away and falls to Earth, and we are very busy getting the shuttle ready to enter orbit. But we're not too busy to notice that our books and pencils are floating in midair. We're in space!

"Shuttle Rockets to Orbit with 5 Aboard"

by John Noble Wilford, The New York Times, June 19, 1983

CAPE CANAVERAL, Fla. — Four men and a woman, the first American woman to go into space, rocketed into orbit today aboard the space shuttle *Challenger* and then launched the first of two satellites in the successful beginning of a busy six-day mission. . . .

[W]hat set this flight apart from the 36 other manned American space missions over the last 22 years was not the cargo but the occupant just behind the two pilots. She was Dr. Sally K. Ride, a 32-year-old physicist who has been in astronaut training since 1978. She is the third woman to fly in space, but the first on an American mission.

A crowd estimated at 250,000 stood in the bright morning sun to watch the seventh shuttle launching, and many of them wore "Ride, Sally Ride" T-shirts. . . .

In the ascent, as the spaceship climbed toward an 184-mile-high orbit, Ride could be heard, in her role as a flight engineer, calling out checklists in a clear, businesslike voice.

Then, relaxing somewhat as the *Challenger* approached orbit, Ride radioed Mission Control, "See you Friday," referring to the crew's planned landing here at the Kennedy Space Center. This would be the first time a shuttle has been brought back to the three-mile runway at its launching base.

And, like any other astronaut after his or her first ascent into orbit, Ride sought to give expression to the thrill of a first flight.

"Have you ever been to Disneyland?" she asked Roy Bridges, the astronaut acting as the crew communicator at Mission Control. "Affirmative," replied Mr. Bridges. "This is definitely an E ticket," Dr. Ride remarked, referring to a ticket that the amusement park used to have for admission to the best rides, including the super roller coaster. . . .

---

1 Which information is in Sally Ride's account but **not** John Noble Wilford's?

Answer Form

1 Ⓐ Ⓑ Ⓒ Ⓓ   **Number**

2 Ⓐ Ⓑ Ⓒ Ⓓ   **Correct**   /2

  A what rockets and engines sound like during a launch

  B who rides the space shuttle with astronaut Sally Ride

  C how long this particular space mission will take

  D how astronauts communicate with Mission Control

2 Which of these **best** describes the difference in focus between the accounts?

A Ride focuses on the first eight and one-half minutes of the launch. Wilford focuses on the entire mission from beginning to end.

B Ride focuses on how the human body responds to being in space. Wilford focuses on how human beings respond to being lonely in space.

C Ride focuses on what it feels like to go into space. Wilford focuses on why Ride going into space is an important event in history.

D Ride focuses on the importance of being the first American woman to go into space. Wilford focuses on the importance of Ride's scientific mission.

3 Look at the table below. It contains sentences from the two passages.

from *To Space and Back*	from "Shuttle Rockets to Orbit with 5 Aboard"
During the next few minutes the empty fuel tank drops away and falls to Earth, and we are very busy getting the shuttle ready to enter orbit. But we're not too busy to notice that our books and pencils are floating in midair. We're in space!	In the ascent, as the spaceship climbed toward an 184-mile-high orbit, Ride could be heard, in her role as a flight engineer, calling out checklists in a clear, businesslike voice.

Describe one way the information in Ride's sentences differs from that found in Wilford's sentences. Use **two** details from the sentences in your answer.

_____

_____

_____

_____

 **Self Check** *Go back and see what you can check off on the Self Check on page 117.*

Read the following history article. Then answer the questions that follow.

from "Ferris's Grand Idea"

by Marcia Amidon Lusted, Cobblestone

1   Daniel Burnham was stumped. He wanted the World's Columbian Exposition to have a centerpiece, something to rival the Eiffel Tower from the Paris exposition of 1889. Not only had the graceful iron-and-steel structure become a landmark recognized around the world, but France's engineering talent now looked superior to America's. "Some distinctive feature is needed," Burnham said to a group of engineers at a weekly dinner in 1891. "Something novel, original, daring, and unique must be designed and built if American engineers are to retain their prestige and standing."

2   Burnham wanted something that would "out-Eiffel Eiffel" . . . to draw people to Chicago.

3   George Washington Gale Ferris, a young engineer from Pittsburgh, Pennsylvania, was present at the banquet that night. Hearing Burnham's words, Ferris recalled an idea he had been working on. He quickly scribbled the design on his dinner napkin. It was something that had never been done before: a revolving . . . wheel, 250 feet in diameter. It would hold more than 2,000 people in 36 cars attached to the wheel's rim. Each car would be as large as a bus and hold 40 (seated) to 60 (standing) people at a time . . . .

4   The wheel was not finished in time for the fair's opening day, May 1, 1893, but by June the engineers were testing it. On the first day of testing with passengers aboard, crowds of spectators ignored the engineers' requests to stand back. Instead, they rushed the wheel and climbed into the cars for the 20-minute ride. Ten minutes were spent getting passengers off and on. This was followed by a 10-minute nonstop single revolution. Ferris's grand idea was a huge success and wildly popular. It quickly became the highlight of the fair.

5   It cost 50 cents to ride the wheel, the same as the price of admission to the fair itself. The huge wheel cost $400,000 to build and maintain during the exposition. That was an enormous expense in those days. But its total earnings were more than $700,000, making a tidy profit for the fair organizers, Ferris, and the investors who had helped him pay for the project.

6   After the fair closed in October, the wheel was dismantled. It was used several more times, including at the St. Louis World's Fair in 1904, but two years later it was sold for scrap metal. It took 200 pounds of dynamite to finally knock the huge wheel off its towers.

7   Ferris's huge structure is gone, but its legacy lives on in almost every amusement park and carnival . . . . Next time you're awed by the views from the top, think of George Ferris and the vision he had to put you there.

Answer Form

1   Ⓐ   Ⓑ   Ⓒ   Ⓓ
2A   Ⓐ   Ⓑ   Ⓒ   Ⓓ
2B   Ⓐ   Ⓑ   Ⓒ   Ⓓ   **Number**
3   Ⓐ   Ⓑ   Ⓒ   Ⓓ   **Correct**   / 4

1   What is the meaning of the word "recalled" as it is used in paragraph 3 of "Ferris's Grand Idea"?

    A   called again

    B   remembered

    C   came up with

    D   invented

2   Answer Parts A and B below.

Part A

What is the meaning of the word "dismantled" as it is used in paragraph 6 of "Ferris's Grand Idea"?

    A   moved off a stage

    B   emptied of people

    C   taken apart

    D   traveled around

Part B

Which of the phrases from the passage best helps the reader understand the meaning of "dismantled"?

    A   "sold for scrap metal"

    B   "knock the huge wheel off"

    C   "used several more times"

    D   "closed in October"

3 Read the following sentence from "Ferris's Grand Idea."

It was something that had never been done before: a revolving . . . wheel, 250 feet in diameter.

What word has a meaning **closest** to the meaning of the word "revolving"?

A turning

B standing

C twisting

D flipping

4 The author of "Ferris's Grand Idea" organizes paragraphs 1 through 3 by identifying a problem that Daniel Burnham had and telling how George Ferris solved it. Identify one sentence that tells the problem Burnham had. Then identify one sentence that tells how Ferris solved Burnham's problem.

Sentence that tells the problem: _____

_____

_____

_____

Sentence that tells the solution: _____

_____

_____

_____

Read the following article. Then answer the questions that follow.

from "The Ferris Wheel"

by Denton J. Snider, World's Fair Studies (1893)

While the Ferris Wheel was in process of construction many people said they would not trust it. A very old man, leaning on his staff one day and looking up at it, declared: "Life is too precious to be risked in that way." But the Wheel started and nearly everybody is taking a ride; men, women and children are seen going up and returning in safety to their friends. Yet some grow pale and get sick at the stomach during the trip; women cry and become hysterical, and sometimes they faint. For most people it is probably a little trial at the start; but there is a feeling that courage needs a taste of discipline when it fears to go where there is no danger. One can often see a workman carried around on the inside of the rim; when the Wheel starts he walks; when it stops for a moment, he inspects a bolt, or taps the megatherion[1] with his hammer, just to hear the ring of the monster's voice.

[1] **Megatherion:** An ancient Greek word that means "mighty beast."

5　Read these sentences from "The Ferris Wheel."

> While the Ferris Wheel was in process of
> construction many people said they would
> not trust it . . . . But the Wheel started and nearly everybody is taking a
> ride; men, women and children are seen going up and returning in safety to
> their friends.

How did the author organize the events described in these sentences?

A　by cause and effect

B　by compare and contrast

C　by problem and solution

D　by order of events

6　Read the following sentence from "The Ferris Wheel."

> One can often see a workman carried around on the inside of the rim; when
> the Wheel starts he walks; when it stops for a moment, he inspects a bolt . . . .

What does the word "inspects" mean in the context of this sentence?

A　removes

B　tightens

C　looks over

D　ignores

Performance Task—Extended Response

7 Think about the articles "Ferris's Grand Idea" and "The Ferris Wheel."
How are the topics of the articles alike? How are the topics different?
How are their points of view different? What are some ways in which those
points of view differ? Use details from both articles to support your answer.

In your answer, be sure to
- tell how the topics of the articles are alike
- tell how the topics of the articles are different
- tell how their points of view are different
- explain the differences in their points of view
- use details from **both** passages to support your answer

Check your writing for correct spelling, grammar, capitalization,
and punctuation.

_____

_____

_____

_____

_____

_____

_____

_____

Unit 4
Craft and Structure in Literature

How are builders and authors alike? For one thing, they both use tools to make a **structure**. Builders use tools such as hammers, nails, and drills. Authors carefully choose words to write literary texts. Builders and authors also use different materials to **craft** (make) their structures. A bridge builder might use steel, an apartment builder might use concrete, and a cabin builder might use wood. The materials from which authors make literary texts are called elements. A poet uses the elements of verses, stanzas, rhyme, and meter to craft a poem. A play writer uses the cast of characters, dialogue, and a setting description to craft a play. Writers of stories and books use paragraphs, dialogue, and chapters.

In this unit, you'll practice figuring out the meanings of unknown words. You'll review the elements used to craft literary texts. Finally, you'll compare how poems, plays, and prose present characters, settings, and events to readers.

✓ Self Check

Before starting this unit, check off the skills you know below. As you complete each lesson, see how many more you can check off!

I know how to:	Before this unit	After this unit
find the meaning of unfamiliar words and phrases in poems, plays, and prose.	☐	☐
compare and contrast first-person and third-person points of view in literary texts.	☐	☐
refer to the elements of poetry when writing or speaking about poems.	☐	☐
refer to the elements of plays when writing or speaking about plays.	☐	☐
explain major differences between poems, plays, and prose.	☐	☐

Understanding Vocabulary in Literary Texts

CCSS

RL.4.4: Determine the meaning of words and phrases as they are used in a text, including those that allude to significant characters found in mythology (e.g., Herculean).

Theme: *Words, Old and New*

Sometimes when you read a story, poem, or play, you'll come across a word or phrase you don't know. When you don't know the meaning of a word, you can often figure it out by looking at the words and sentences around it. You can use the word's **context**.

Let's practice finding the meaning of a word. Read the story below.

The Search

When I returned home after a long summer day of fun, I realized I'd lost my favorite baseball cap. So I went looking everywhere for it. I walked to the baseball field. I climbed up into Haruki's tree house. I waded in the creek where Juan and I caught frogs. And then I went to the next dozen places. I wandered far and wide in my search. My odyssey ended where it had begun, back at home. Despite my long journey, I'd failed to find my cap. That is, until I finally sat down. It had been in my back pocket all along!

Now read the story again. Find the sentence with the word *odyssey*. Circle that word. Then underline the sentences that come before and after that sentence.

In the table below, write down the sentence that follows the one with the word *odyssey*. Then, based on the context, write a definition of *odyssey* in the last row.

Context Clue Before	Sentence with Word	Context Clue After
I **wandered far and wide** in my search.	My **odyssey** ended where it had begun, back at home.	_____ _____ _____
Meaning of word: An *odyssey* is _____ .		

Context clues aren't always just before or after an unknown word. Sometimes you have to hunt far and wide in a text to find them. But it's worth it. Stories, poems, and plays are more fun to read when you can figure out all the words, both old and new!

Read the first paragraph of a story about a girl who badly wants to win a race.

Genre: **Realistic Fiction**

Out to Win   *by Wendy Barry*

As the annual track meet approached, all I could think about was Anna Banks. She'd beaten me in the 400-meter run the past three years—and always by just a step. I'd had enough of second place. This year, I was out to win. I couldn't think about anything else. I became **obsessed** with beating Anna. I thought about that one thing, winning, all the time. I did more than think, of course. I practiced my starts. And I ran and ran and ran.

(continued)

Explore how to answer this question: *"What is the meaning of the word* obsessed *as it is used in the story?"*

The word *obsessed* describes how the narrator is thinking about Anna and the race. Reread the text, but this time underline any context clues that help you figure out what *obsessed* means.

The table below will help you organize the context clues you underlined above. Write at least one context clue in each empty column.

Context Clue Before	Sentence with Word	Context Clue After
_____ _____ _____	"I became **obsessed** with beating Anna."	_____ _____ _____

What do the context clues tell you about the meaning of the word *obsessed*? They tell you that the narrator spent nearly all of her time thinking about how to beat Anna in the race.

On the lines below, write the meaning of the word *obsessed* in your own words.

The word *obsessed* means _____

_____

_____ .

Continue reading about the girl who wants to win a race. Use the Close Reading and the Hint to help you answer the question.

Close Reading

Underline nearby clues that help you figure out the meaning of the word *nemesis*.

(continued from page 162)

The day of the race, I was more than ready. The starting gun fired. Anna and I soon ran ahead of the others. We raced to the finish line. I didn't even know who'd won at first. Then I heard—it was me! Anna rushed right over, smiling, and shook my hand. "You were great!" she said. "Good race!"

I realized right then that I'd been looking at this all wrong. Before, I'd been thinking of Anna like she was some powerful enemy out to destroy me. But Anna wasn't my **nemesis** at all. She had no urge to crush me. In fact, she had helped make me better than I ever would have been without her.

Hint

Anna turns out to be nice. Is she the kind of person you would think of as an "enemy"?

Circle the correct answer.

At the end of the story, the narrator says, "But Anna wasn't my nemesis at all." What does the word *nemesis* mean?

A   a poor loser

B   a very fast runner

C   a kind or helpful friend

D   a source of harm or defeat

✎ **Show Your Thinking**

Write down the sentences that helped you figure out the meaning of the word *nemesis*.

Sentence Before	Sentence with Word	Sentence After
	"But Anna wasn't my nemesis at all."	

Read the lyric poem. Use the Study Buddy and the Close Reading to guide your reading.

Wow! There are many words I don't know. But I know what to do: I'll circle words I'm not sure about, then underline any context clues.

Close Reading

The speaker imagines the catfish as half cat ("feline") and half fish. **Circle** any words that tell you how he thinks those halves get along.

Does the feline half ever catch the fishy half? **Underline** words or sentences that tell you what the speaker imagines happening.

Genre: **Lyric Poem**

The Catfish

by Oliver Herford, The Book of Humorous Verse

The saddest fish that swims the briny ocean,
    The Catfish I bewail.
I cannot even think without emotion
    Of his distressful tail.
When with my pencil once I tried to draw one,
    (I dare not show it here)
Mayhap it is because I never saw one,
    The picture looked so queer.
I vision him half feline and half fishy,
    A paradox in twins,
Unmixable as vitriol[1] and vichy[2]—
    A thing of fur and fins.
A feline Tantalus, forever chasing
    His fishy self to rend;
His finny self forever self-effacing
    In circles without end.
This tale may have a Moral running through it
    As Aesop had in his;
If so, dear reader, you are welcome to it,
    If you know what it is!

[1] **Vitriol:** a dangerous chemical that can damage things; an acid

[2] **Vichy:** an old word for sparkling mineral water; vichy is safe to drink

---

Hints

Use the Hints on this page to help you answer the questions.

> The words around *bewail* include *saddest*, *emotion*, and *distressful*.

1 Read these lines from the poem.

> The saddest fish that swims the briny ocean,
>   The Catfish I bewail.
> I cannot even think without emotion
>   Of his distressful tail.

What is the meaning of *bewail* as it is used in the poem?

A　to wonder about

B　to feel confused about

C　to draw a picture of

D　to feel deep sorrow for

> How well would a real cat and fish get along?

2 Read these lines from the poem.

> I vision him half feline and half fishy,
>   A paradox in twins,
> Unmixable as vitriol and vichy—

What is the meaning of *paradox* as it used in the poem?

A　something whose parts don't seem to go together

B　a fish that has fur and looks a lot like a cat

C　someone who is confused and spins around

D　a make-believe animal with two different heads

> Does the "feline half" ever get what it wants? Does it ever catch the "fishy half"?

3 The poet imagines a catfish as having a head forever chasing its own fishy tail. Given this picture, explain what it means to call someone a *Tantalus*. Use two details to support your response.

_____

_____

_____

_____

_____

_____

Read the poem. Then answer the questions that follow.

Can't

by Edgar Guest, A Heap O Livin'

Can't is the worst word that's written or spoken;
    Doing more harm here than slander and lies;
On it is many a strong spirit broken,
    And with it many a good purpose dies.
5 It springs from the lips of the thoughtless each morning
    And robs us of courage we need through the day:
It rings in our ears like a timely-sent warning
    And laughs when we falter and fall by the way.

Can't is the father of feeble endeavor,
10   The parent of terror and half-hearted work;
It weakens the efforts of artisans clever,
    And makes of the toiler an indolent shirk.
It poisons the soul of the man with a vision,
    It stifles in infancy many a plan;
15 It greets honest toiling with open derision
    And mocks at the hopes and the dreams of a man.

Can't is a word none should speak without blushing;
    To utter it should be a symbol of shame;
Ambition and courage it daily is crushing;
20   It blights a man's purpose and shortens his aim.
Despise it with all of your hatred of error;
    Refuse it the lodgment it seeks in your brain;
Arm against it as a creature of terror,
    And all that you dream of you some day shall gain.

25   *Can't* is the word that is foe to ambition,
      An enemy ambushed to shatter your will;
   Its prey is forever the man with a mission
      And bows but to courage and patience and skill.
   Hate it, with hatred that's deep and undying,
30   For once it is welcomed 'twill break any man;
   Whatever the goal you are seeking, keep trying
      And answer this demon by saying: "I *can*."

1   What does the word "falter" mean as it is used in line 8 of the poem?

A   to move without confidence

B   to walk quickly and with a purpose

C   to go forward without stopping

D   to think about how to finish a task

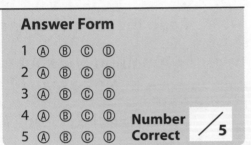

Answer Form

1 Ⓐ Ⓑ Ⓒ Ⓓ
2 Ⓐ Ⓑ Ⓒ Ⓓ
3 Ⓐ Ⓑ Ⓒ Ⓓ
4 Ⓐ Ⓑ Ⓒ Ⓓ   **Number**
5 Ⓐ Ⓑ Ⓒ Ⓓ   **Correct**   /5

2   Read the following lines from the poem.

   Can't is the father of feeble endeavor,
      The parent of terror and half-hearted work;
  It weakens the efforts of artisans clever,
      And makes of the toiler an indolent shirk.

What is the meaning of "endeavor" as it is used in the first line above?

A   child

B   weakness

C   fear

D   effort

3 What does the word "vision" mean as it is used in line 13 of the poem?

A sight

B ghost

C dream

D future

4 Read the following lines from the poem.

Ambition and courage it daily is crushing;
  It blights a man's purpose and shortens his aim.

What does the word "blights" mean as it is used in the second line above?

A lifts

B harms

C leaves

D weighs

5 Read the following lines from the poem.

Can't is the word that is foe to ambition,
  An enemy ambushed to shatter your will;
Its prey is forever the man with a mission
  And bows but to courage and patience and skill.

The first line above uses the phrase "foe to ambition." What is a "foe to ambition"?

A a friend who helps you finish a job

B a person who gives up on a task

C an enemy who works against your goals

D a person fighting to overcome a bad habit

✓ **Self Check** *Go back and see what you can check off on the Self Check on page 159.*

Comparing Points of View

CCSS

RL.4.6: Compare and contrast the point of view from which different stories are narrated, including the difference between first- and third-person narrations.

Theme: *School Stories*

Every story has a **narrator**, or a person telling the story. And every narrator has a **point of view**, or a way of looking at and thinking about what happens in the story.

Look at the cartoons below. Then finish each sentence on the blank lines.

The two main types of narration are **first person** and **third person**. The table below tells you clues you can use to spot these types of narration.

Point of View	Description of Narrator	Pronoun Clues
First person	a character in the story	As **I** walked down the hall, everyone looked at **me** because. . . .
Third person	a teller outside the story	As **Martha** walked down the hall, people stared at **her**. This was because. . . .

Understanding a narrator's point of view takes more than just identifying first person or third person. You also have to pay attention to what the narrator thinks and feels. A narrator can be happy or sad, fair or unfair, excited or bored, and anything else a person can be.

When you read, pay attention not just to what narrators say but also how they say it. You'll get the fullest, richest sense of their points of view.

Read the first part of a story about a boy going on a school trip to a museum.

Genre: **Realistic Fiction**

Just a Bunch of Rocks and Bones   *by Watson Hamish*

I was looking forward to my first field trip at my new school. We were going to The Museum of Natural History, which sounded pretty interesting to me. That is, until my new friend Barry started talking about it. We were on the bus on our way there, and Barry says, "I'm telling you, Russ, we went last year, and it's so boring—mostly just a bunch of rocks and bones."

Oh, no, I thought. *There's nothing worse than being bored, especially when you were looking forward to something.* Suddenly the trip seemed ruined. Our bus trudged into the museum's parking lot, and we all dragged ourselves outside.

(continued)

Explore how to answer this question: *"Is this story told in first- or third-person narration?"*

The question asks whether the narrator is a character inside the story (first person) or someone outside of the story (third person). Look for pronouns that help you figure this out.

The first two sentences of the story are reprinted below. As you read them, circle some words that tell you whether this story is told in first- or third-person narration.

I was looking forward to my first field trip at my new school. We were going

to The Museum of Natural History, which sounded pretty interesting to me.

On the lines below, tell whether the story is told in first-person or third-person narration. Then explain how you know this, using details from the sentences as evidence.

_____

_____

_____

_____

_____

Continue reading about Russ's trip to the museum. Use the Close Reading and the Hint to help you answer the question.

Close Reading

A narrator's thoughts and feelings affect how he or she describes events. **Underline** any words, both here and on page 170, that show the narrator's thoughts or feelings.

(continued from page 170)

    Sweating under the hot sun, I glumly looked around. Then I noticed a statue of a small, perky dinosaur poking its head out of some bushes. *Hey*, I thought. *This doesn't look so bad.*

    A tour guide met us and took our class around the museum. Barry was right in one way. There were a lot of rocks and bones. But what rocks! We saw cool fossils, sparkling gemstones, and even meteors from space. And the bones were even better. One gallery featured skeletons of mastodons and a saber-toothed cat. Another had dinosaurs, including part of a *T. Rex*. I was already hoping we'd come back next year. But I don't think I'm ready to tell Barry that.

Hint

How do the words you underlined show how Russ's feelings change over time?

Circle the correct answer.

How do Russ's feelings about the field trip to the museum change from the beginning of the story to its end?

A Russ is excited at first, becomes unhappy when he steps off the bus, and then ends up being scared of Barry.

B Russ is worried that he'll be bored, becomes more interested when he sees the statue, and then has a good time.

C Russ looks forward to seeing the museum, becomes worried about being bored, and ends up enjoying his time there.

D Russ wonders whether the museum will be interesting, realizes that it is not, and ends up accepting that he has to be there.

✎ Show Your Thinking

 Think about Russ's friend Barry. What is Barry's point of view toward the field trip? With a friend, talk about how Barry would narrate this story.

Read the story. Use the Study Buddy and the Close Reading to guide your reading.

Genre: **Science Fiction**

So, I wonder—what is the narrator's point of view? I'll look for words that show how the narrator thinks or feels about characters and events.

Close Reading

How does Hoshi feel before going into the 3-D room? **Underline** a detail that shows this.

Circle two words that tell whether this story is told by a first- or third-person narrator.

If Only This Were Real   by Jing Wu

1   Hoshi stared at the clock at the front of the classroom. The school day was almost over. She couldn't wait to go play with her friend Jeri. They had created a new game in a 3-D room on Deck C, and it was so much fun, it made everything better. At least their new teacher, Ms. Vox-23, was better than their last Class A instructional robot.

2   Ms. Vox-23 finished the lesson, then said what she always said: "Enjoy the rest of your afternoon! It's another lovely day."

3   Hoshi looked out the window into the blackness of space. Every hour of every day looked the same. She had spent half her life in space, traveling to a planet in another galaxy. She would be 15 by the time they got there.

4   After class, Hoshi and Jeri ran straight to Deck C and entered one of the 3-D rooms. These rooms could create any scene a person imagined. Jeri excitedly pressed some buttons. Then she said, "Computer: Run the program *Old School on a Big Hill on Real Earth*." The bare room instantly changed into an old classroom. A dusty blackboard hung behind an old wooden desk. Sunlight from the big windows filled the room. When Hoshi and Jeri looked out the window, they could see white clouds, blue sky, flowering trees, green grass, and a playground. They asked their human teacher, Ms. Ryan, if they could go outside for recess.

5   *If only this were real*, Hoshi thought. *Maybe someday, in the future, things will be this good.*

Hints

Which choice has pronouns showing the narrator is a person outside of the story?

Use the Hints on this page to help you answer the questions.

1 Which sentence from "If Only This Were Real" contains the best evidence that the story is written in third-person narration?

   A   "The school day was almost over."

   B   "She couldn't wait to go play with her friend Jeri."

   C   "'Enjoy the rest of your afternoon!'"

   D   "Jeri excitedly pressed some buttons."

How does the narrator seem to feel about Hoshi and Jeri's lives aboard the space ship?

2 Imagine you could ask the narrator of "If Only This Were Real" to say, in one sentence, his or her feelings about what it would be like to live in space. What would the narrator most likely say?

   A   Hoshi should be more grateful for the wonders about her.

   B   Technology will cure the problems involved in space travel.

   C   The challenges of space travel are too difficult to overcome.

   D   Living in space would rob people of some simple pleasures.

Good details to include in your answer would be the exact pronouns that each narrator uses.

3 Think about the story "Just a Bunch of Rocks and Bones" on pages 170 and 171. Explain how the point of view of that story is different than the point of view of "If Only This Were Real." Use at least two details from each story to support your answer.

_____

_____

_____

_____

_____

_____

_____

_____

173

Read the two stories. Then answer the questions that follow.

Putting It Off

by Alan McMullen

1   "Come sit with me! I'll help you study for your test, Serena!" called Mom. I rolled my eyes. It was a whole week before the big math test, and I didn't feel like studying yet.

2   "Mom!" I wailed. "Can't I finish watching this show on the science channel first? It's educational! Plus, if I study now, I'll just forget everything before next week."

3   Mom sighed. "Go ahead and finish the show, I guess. But I won't be able to help you study later."

4   "That's okay, Mom. I'll just study alone later." She gave me a look that showed that she knew I didn't intend to study. I wish she understood that I do my best work at the last minute!

5   I relaxed into the couch again. I was only halfway watching the science channel. Mostly I was peeling stickers from a sheet and arranging them artfully on the cover of my math notebook. It was a lot more fun than studying, that's for sure.

6   Once I got the cover just the way I wanted it, I put my notebook and stickers away and went to the kitchen to have dinner. (Macaroni and cheese, my favorite!) Shortly after that, it was time for bed. Of course I hadn't studied. Why would I? The test was a whole week away.

7   The next morning, I walked into math class. I was well-rested and refreshed, but everyone else looked sleepy. "What's going on?" I asked my friend Megan. "Why's everybody so tired?"

8   "I stayed up until almost 10 studying for the test," said Megan. "Didn't you?"

9   "Uh, no. It's next week, right?" I started to feel a little nervous.

10   "Serena! Don't you remember? Mr. Gordon changed the day of the test from next Friday to this Friday! You didn't study at all?" Megan looked at me with her eyes wide. I sunk into my seat. If only I'd let Mom help me study last night, I might have a chance at passing the test. Next time, I probably shouldn't wait until the last minute.

Trick or Treat

by Bessie Chevalier

1   Terry hid his face behind his science book so no one would see him laugh. Everybody knew that when Terry laughed when nobody else was laughing, somebody was about to get pranked. This time it was his teacher, Mr. Mason. Terry had put a rubber spider on Mr. Mason's chair and couldn't wait to see what happened when his teacher sat down.

2   "Good morning, class!" said Mr. Mason as he breezed into the room. "Let's get started, shall we?" he said, grabbing his science book. He pulled his chair out and got ready to sit. Terry couldn't help himself and let out a squeaky laugh.

3   Mr. Mason froze. "Terry? Is there something you need to tell me?" he asked.

4   "No, Mr. Mason," Terry answered, but the huge smile on his face told the truth.

5   Mr. Mason leaned over and looked at the seat of his chair. There, right in the middle, was a big, black spider. Mr. Mason picked up the rubber spider and walked over to Terry's desk.

6   "Terry, your pranks are getting tiresome," Mr. Mason said. The other students nodded. At first, Terry's pranks had been funny. But nobody could remember a day when he hadn't played a trick on someone in the class. "I need you to go sit in the hall for ten minutes and think about how you're making people feel with your pranks."

7   Terry left the class and sat against the wall in the hallway. His smile was gone. He didn't really feel bad, though. He was mostly mad that Mr. Mason had figured out his prank before he sat down. Terry had really wanted to see Mr. Mason's reaction.

8   A few minutes later, the classroom door opened. "You can come back in now, Terry," said Mr. Mason. Terry hopped up and walked back to his desk. "All right, let's get back to business," Mr. Mason continued. "Did everyone bring their permission slips for the field trip to the ice cream factory?"

9   Terry's eyes widened. Field trip? Ice cream factory? He didn't remember ever hearing about this. But all around him, everyone was reaching into their desks and pulling out permission slips.

10   "Mr. Mason! I don't have a permission slip!" Terry wailed. He couldn't believe he was going to miss such a great trip.

11   Mr. Mason grinned. "How does it feel to be pranked, Terry?" he asked.

12   Terry realized there was no field trip. He heaved a sigh of relief. "It felt awful, Mr. Mason," he answered. Terry suddenly realized that he was getting tired of his pranks, too.

1 Which statement comparing the points of view in "Putting It Off" and "Trick or Treat" is correct?

A Both stories have first-person narration.

B Both stories have third-person narration.

C Both stories describe the thoughts of the main characters in the story.

D Both stories are told from the point of view of many characters in the story.

2 The table below is about the stories "Putting It Off" and "Trick or Treat."

Story	Narrator
"Putting It Off"	Serena
"Trick or Treat"	

Which of the following should go in the blank space in the table?

A Terry

B Mr. Mason

C an unnamed student inside the story

D a person outside of the story

3 Compare and contrast the types of narration in "Putting It Off" and "Trick or Treat." Use at least **one** detail from **each** story to support your answer.

_____

_____

_____

_____

_____

_____

✓ **Self Check**   *Go back and see what you can check off on the Self Check on page 159.*

Elements of Poetry

CCSS
RL.4.5: [R]efer to the structural elements of poems (e.g., verse, rhythm, meter) . . . when writing or speaking about a text.

Theme: *Humorous Poems*

A poem has a structure that's made of both elements you see on the page, such as **verses** and **stanzas**, and elements you hear, such as **rhythm** and **meter**. As you read the poem below, notice how it looks. If you get to read it aloud, notice how it sounds.

Bigfoot's Complaint
by John Hansen

Why do they have to call me *that*?
I'm more than just a pair of feet.
If humans took a closer look,
They'd see my eyes are rather sweet.

But I walk these woods in hiding,
My footprints left in mud and snow.
The rest of me they'll never see
So I am called by what they know.

Now, read the table below. It defines some of the elements that many poems have.

Element	Definition
Verse	one line of a poem; often just called a "line"
Stanza	a group of verses that describes an image or idea
Rhyme	words at the end of two or more verses that have the same sound
Rhyme scheme	a pattern of rhyming words in a poem
Rhythm	a pattern of weak and STRONG sounds throughout a poem
Meter	a verse's number of syllables plus its pattern of weak and STRONG sounds

In the poem above, do the following: (1) Draw a line under the first verse. (2) Draw boxes around the stanzas. (3) Circle end words that rhyme, then connect them with a line. (4) As a class, count the number of syllables in each of the first two verses.

When you pay attention to both the look and the sound of poetry, you'll do more than just think about what the poem means. You'll start to feel it, too!

Read the first part of a poem about a dog who loves to go for walks.

Genre: **Narrative Poem**

Walking Big Willie   *by Clary Barton*

While I am working hard at school,
To master math and this and that,
At home Big Willie sleeps a lot
And dreams of chasing neighbors' cats.

Big Willie shakes himself awake
When through the door I come at three.
A furry bullet knocks me down.
A leash is dropped upon my knee.

(continued)

Explore how to answer this question: *"Each verse of this poem has the same meter. What is this meter? In your answer, identify the number of syllables in a verse. Then describe the pattern of weak and STRONG syllables in a verse."*

First, find the number of syllables in each verse.

The first two verses of the poem are shown below. Count the number of syllables in each verse. Then write the number of syllables next to the end of the verse.

Verse 1: While I am work-ing hard at school,   _____ syllables

Verse 2: To mas-ter math and this and that,   _____ syllables

Now, think about the pattern of weak *(weak)* and strong *(STRONG)* syllables in each verse.

Verse 1: While I am work-ing hard at school,   *(while I am WORK-ing HARD at SCHOOL,)*

Verse 2: To mas-ter math and this and that,   *(to MAS-ter MATH and THIS and THAT,)*

A complete description of this poem's meter is: Each verse has _____ syllables.

The syllables in each verse follow a pattern of weak-STRONG, _____

_____

Continue reading about Big Willie going for a walk. Use the Close Reading and the Hint to help you answer the question.

Close Reading

Circle any word at the end of a verse that rhymes with a word at the end of a different verse. Then, **draw lines** to connect the pairs of rhyming words.

(continued from page 178)

We're on the street. No time to waste.
A million squirrels must be treed.
Some cats must be tormented next.
Will does this all at double speed.

Around the block and up the street,
He travels at the speed of sound,
And I, attached to him by leash,
Am led around and 'round and 'round.

I must confess I like the speed.
It's fun to travel zip–zam–zoom.
But sometimes when I'm out with Will,
I wonder, who is walking whom?

Hint

Look at the words you circled in the poem. Which verses of each stanza are they in?

Circle the correct answer.

Which statement describes the rhyme scheme of the stanzas above?

A All of the verses in each stanza have end words that rhyme.

B The first and third verses in each stanza have end words that rhyme.

C The second and fourth verses in each stanza have end words that rhyme.

D The third and fourth verses in each stanza have end words that rhyme.

✎ **Show Your Thinking**

 With a partner, write a four-line poem with the same rhyme scheme as the first stanza of "Walking Big Willie."

Read the poem. Use the Study Buddy and the Close Reading to guide your reading.

I usually have to read a poem a few times. The first time, I try to figure out what it means. The second time, I try to figure out what elements of poetry the poet chose to use.

Close Reading

Next to the first stanza, **write down** the number of verses, the meter of the first verse, and the pattern of rhyming words.

This poem tells a story. It has a beginning, a middle, and an end. **Label** the parts with a "B," an "M," and an "E."

Genre: **Narrative Poem**

A Tragic Story

by W. M. Thackeray, The Book of Humorous Verse

There lived a sage[1] in days of yore,
And he a handsome pigtail wore;
But wondered much and sorrowed more,
Because it hung behind him.

He mused upon this curious case,
And swore he'd change the pigtail's place,
And have it hanging at his face,
Not dangling there behind him.

Says he, "The mystery I've found,—
I'll turn me round,"—he turned him round;
But still it hung behind him.

Then round and round, and out and in,
All day the puzzled sage did spin;
In vain—it mattered not a pin,—
The pigtail hung behind him.

And right and left, and round about,
And up and down, and in and out,
He turned; but still the pigtail stout
Hung steadily behind him.

And though his efforts never slack,
And though he twist and twirl and tack,
Alas! still faithful to his back,
The pigtail hangs behind him.

[1] **Sage:** a wise person

Hints

Sometimes you won't be able to read a poem aloud. If you still need to figure out the pattern of weak and STRONG syllables, gently tap the pattern with your fingers.

Use the Hints on this page to help you answer the questions.

1 Here is the first stanza of "A Tragic Story."

There lived a sage in days of yore,
And he a handsome pigtail wore;
But wondered much and sorrowed more,
Because it hung behind him.

On the lines below, describe the following about this stanza:

The meter of the first verse, using the words "syllables," "weak," and "STRONG": _____

_____

_____

_____

The rhyme scheme of the stanza: _____

_____

_____

_____

The stanzas tell different parts of the story. It might help to read the poem again. Next to each stanza, write a sentence summarizing it.

2 Briefly tell what happens in each stanza of the poem.

Stanza one: _____

_____

Stanza two: _____

_____

Stanza three: _____

_____

Stanzas four *and* five: _____

_____

Stanza six: _____

_____

Read the poem. Then answer the questions that follow.

Revenge

by Felicia Witt

"A very fine Friday," Fiona did say,
And set out to write up a plan for her day.
"The first thing I'll do," said Fiona with flair
"Is find out who planted this gum in my hair."

5   For Fiona, just moments ago, had tried prying
Her head from her pillow, which made her start crying.
For stuck 'twixt her head and the pillow so dewy
Was a wad of gum—sticky, icky, and chewy.

"Who did this thing?" asked Fiona, whose eyes
10   Narrowed to slits of the tiniest size.
"Maybe a kid on whom I've played a prank—
But that's nearly everyone!" Fiona's heart sank.

Yes, it's true, our Fiona was known as a trickster
Neither parents nor doctors nor teachers could fix her.
15   Every soul in her school had at some point been bitten
By her tricks, though she seemed like an innocent kitten.

So it made all the sense in the world, she admitted,
that the gum in her hair was a message to quit it.
"I've played some great tricks on that crybaby, Jack.
20   Bet he put this old gum in my hair to get back."

She would have to get back at that back-getter, Jack,
And she thoughtfully planned out the perfect attack.
Jack's habits were something that Fiona knew
So she set out to replace his shampoo with glue.

25   But Fiona, in haste to avenge her gummed head,
Had missed all the gum wrappers under her bed.
She'd forgotten her own constant habit of chewing
And that the past night, that's what she'd been doing.

Answer the questions. Mark your answers to questions 1–3 on the Answer Form to the right.

1 The poet of "Revenge" uses long verses with a fast rhythm to create a certain feeling. What is the feeling she **most likely** wants readers to experience?

A how upset Fiona is about finding the gum in her hair

B how tired Fiona is just after waking up in the morning

C how happy Fiona is thinking about all the pranks she's played

D how bad Fiona feels about all the tricks she's played on others

2 Which statement supports the idea that the poem uses a particular type of meter to help make its rhythm?

A Some verses look a lot longer on the page than others do.

B Each stanza has four lines.

C All of the verses have the same number of syllables.

D Each stanza contains two complete sentences.

3 What is the **main** purpose of each stanza in "Revenge"?

A to make lines that rhyme in pairs

B to tell one part of Fiona's story

C to show when Fiona talks to herself

D to help the reader speak the poem aloud

4 On the lines below, describe the following about the poem "Revenge":

The total number of stanzas: _____

The number of verses in each stanza: _____

The rhyme scheme of the first stanza: _____

_____

_____

_____

The meter of the first verse, using the words "syllables," "weak," and "STRONG":

_____

_____

_____

5 State what the poet tells readers in the last stanza to make the early stanzas seem even funnier. Explain your answer, referring to both events and elements of the poem.

_____

_____

_____

_____

_____

_____

 **Self Check** *Go back and see what you can check off on the Self Check on page 159.*

Lesson 20   Part 1: Introduction 👥

Elements of Plays

CCSS

RL.4.5: [R]efer to the structural elements of . . . drama (e.g., casts of characters, settings, descriptions, dialogue, stage directions) when writing or speaking about a text.

Theme: *Comedies*

A **play** (also called a **drama**) is written to be performed on stage. A play's **script** is a set of directions that tells you the play's features. It tells who the characters are, what they say and do, and what the setting is. A person who writes a play is a **playwright**.

Read the scene below. On the line next to "Setting," write where the scene takes place. Then complete the stage direction by writing what you think will happen next.

Name of Play: The Surly Chefs

Setting: _____

HEAD CHEF [*to a hotel guest*]: So, you don't like our pies, do you? Maybe you'd like another taste, eh?

[*The three chefs then*_____
_____.]

Read the table below. It tells about some features that usually appear in play scripts.

Feature	Description
Cast of characters	lists all characters who appear in the play
Setting	tells where and when the play takes place
Dialogue	tells exactly what the actors say on stage
Stage directions	tells about any actions or movements on stage
Descriptions	gives details about how settings or characters look

When reading a play, pay attention to all of its features, not just its dialogue. If you only read what the characters say, you're missing the big picture. Try to picture in your head the play's setting, the stage directions, and how the characters look, act, and sound.

Read the first part of a play about two men who get a big scare inside a pyramid.

Genre: **Play**

Where's My Mummy? *by Silas Johnson*

Cast of Characters: WILBUR, ROY, GLEN, *a* MUMMY

Setting: The inside of a pyramid in Egypt

[Two workers, WILBUR *and* ROY, *shovel dirt into a wheelbarrow. Oil lamps light the dark chamber, which includes a* MUMMY'S *tomb made of stone.]*

WILBUR [*shivering*]: Oooooh, Roy. This place gives me the creeps!

ROY: What's to be afraid of, Wilbur? Just get to work so we can get out of here.

[The cover of the tomb creaks open. A wrapped hand reaches from inside.]

WILBUR: Did you hear that? I heard something. [*He sees the* MUMMY'S *hand and starts shaking.*] And now I see something that I really don't want to be seeing!

(continued)

Explore how to answer this question: *"Which two features of the script tell the actor playing Wilbur that he should act scared?"*

This question asks you to find information in the play that tells an actor how to perform his part. Part of what Wilbur says and does is given in the table below. Write the rest on the blank lines.

Feature	Example
Dialogue	WILBUR [*shivering*]: This place gives me _____!
Stage directions	[*He sees the* MUMMY'S *hand and* _____.]

Fill in the blanks to show how an actor playing Wilbur would know how to play his part.

An actor playing Wilbur would know he should act scared because his first line of _____

says, "This place gives me the creeps," and his _____

say, "[*He sees the* MUMMY'S *hand and* _____.]"

Continue reading about Wilbur and Roy in the pyramid. Use the Close Reading and the Hint to help you answer the question.

Close Reading

What does the Mummy do after Wilbur and Roy start to scream? **Underline** the sentence that tells you what the Mummy does.

(continued from page 186)

[*The* Mummy *climbs out of the tomb, moans, and walks toward them.* Wilbur *and* Roy *scream. Then the* Mummy *starts laughing.*]

Roy: Hey, I'd know that laugh anywhere. Is that you, Glen?

Glen [*unwrapping his head*]: Pretty good costume, don't you think?

Roy: Not bad. But what did you do with the real mummy?

Glen: What mummy? There was nobody in there.

[*Just then a* Mummy *walks slowly toward them from the shadows.* Wilbur, Roy, *and* Glen *scream, turn, and run.*]

Hint

How does Roy figure out who the first Mummy might be?

Read the question. Then write your answer on the lines provided.

When would an audience start to think that the first Mummy isn't real? Use details from the play, such as dialogue and stage directions, to explain your answer.

_____

_____

_____

_____

_____

✎ | **Show Your Thinking**
_____

 Look at the answer you wrote above. With a partner, discuss what details from the play helped you understand when an audience might start to think that the first Mummy wasn't real.

Read the play. Use the Study Buddy and the Close Reading to guide your reading.

When I read a play, I imagine how the action looks on a stage. For example, when I read about Young Light stamping her foot and pounding her fists, I picture in my mind what that looks and sounds like.

Close Reading

How does Young Light feel about what's going on? **Underline** one line of dialogue *and* one stage direction that show how she feels.

How do we know what it sounds like when Young Light "wakes up" the clouds? **Draw a box** around the sentences that tell you what that sounds like.

Genre: **Play**

The Lightning Tantrum *by Hillary Sturm*

1   *Cast of Characters:* YOUNG LIGHT, MOTHER LIGHT, FATHER LIGHT

2   *Setting: A colorful, cloud-filled sky at late evening. The light dims on three figures dressed in bright white gowns.*

3   YOUNG LIGHT: I'm tired of behaving! It's boring, and I don't want to be quiet! And I really don't want to go to bed yet!

4   MOTHER LIGHT: Young Light, I know you don't want to go to bed yet, but that's the way it has to be.

5   FATHER LIGHT: During the day you can play as much as you like. But when night comes, you've got to go to bed.

6   YOUNG LIGHT: But why? Why can't I play at night?

7   MOTHER LIGHT: Because there can't be light in the sky at night. That's when people on Earth are sleeping.

8   YOUNG LIGHT: It's not fair! [YOUNG LIGHT *stamps her foot. Then she begins pounding her fists against the sky.*]

9   FATHER LIGHT: Stop that! You'll wake up the whole sky!

10   YOUNG LIGHT: So? I want to wake up the sky! Hey, Clouds! Wake up! [*There's a low rumbling sound that gradually grows very loud. A flash of light is followed by a loud BOOM!*]

11   YOUNG LIGHT: Ha ha! I woke up the Clouds! RUMBLE!

12   MOTHER LIGHT [*shaking her head*]: Oh, dear. I guess the people on Earth will have a big thunder and lightning storm tonight. I'm afraid no one will be getting much sleep!

Hints

The setting is where and when the action takes place.

The name of the play is *The Lightning Tantrum*. What kinds of things do kids say and do when they "throw a tantrum"?

If the stage directions were left out, what would not be in the play? What actions and sounds would be missing?

Use the Hints on this page to help you answer the questions.

1 How would the information about the setting at the start of the script help people who wanted to put the play on the stage?

     A It gives ideas for how the stage and the actors look.

     B It tells what the story is going to be about.

     C It explains how the actors should move on stage.

     D It suggests that a thunderstorm is coming.

2 In the play, choose one line of dialogue and one stage direction that tells the actor playing Young Light how to act upset and angry. Write your choices in the table below.

How Upset Is Young Light?	
Something she says:	
Something she does:	

3 Explain why the stage directions in the second half of the play are important to what happens. Use at least two details from the play to support your answer.

_____

_____

_____

_____

_____

_____

Read the play. Then answer the questions that follow.

The Endless Tale

by Octavia Louis

1   *Setting: A long time ago in a grand palace.*

2   *Cast of Characters:* KING, PRINCESS, FIRST STORYTELLER, SECOND STORYTELLER, LORDS AND LADIES, GUARDS

3   [*The* KING *sits on a cushion in the great hall. The* PRINCESS *sits on a cushion by him. In front of them sits the* FIRST STORYTELLER. *The* LORDS AND LADIES *sit near by.*]

4   FIRST STORYTELLER: "Then the prince married the princess and they were happy forever and ever." [*There is a pause.*]

5   KING: Go on! [*The* FIRST STORYTELLER *hangs his head.*] Go on, I say!

6   FIRST STORYTELLER: That is all, your Majesty.

7   KING [*outraged*]: All!

8   FIRST STORYTELLER: The prince married the princess. There is nothing more to tell.

9   KING: I cannot bear so short a story!

10   PRINCESS: Why, father; for three months we have listened to it!

11   KING: 'Tis short, I say! I bid you make it longer, sir!

12   FIRST STORYTELLER: I cannot, Sire. The prince married the princess. There is nothing—

13   KING: Throw him out of the palace, guards! Off with his head! [GUARDS *seize* FIRST STORYTELLER.]

14   PRINCESS: Father!

15   LORDS AND LADIES: Your Majesty!

16   PRINCESS: Spare his life!

17   FIRST STORYTELLER: Let me keep my head, Sire!

18   KING: Why should you keep it? You do not use it.

19   STORYTELLER: For three months I have used it, Sire!

20   KING: Your story is too short, I say! Away with him, guards! Away! [GUARDS *take out the* FIRST STORYTELLER.] Bid another Storyteller come! [*A* GUARD *admits the* SECOND STORYTELLER, *who bows before the* KING *and* PRINCESS.]

21   KING: Sir, hear me. You must tell a story that will last forever.

22   SECOND STORYTELLER: I hear, O King!

23   KING: If you can do this, you shall marry my daughter and be King after me.

24   SECOND STORYTELLER: I hear, O King!

25   KING: If you fail, you shall lose your head. Begin! And remember, the story must go on forever. Now again I say, begin!

26   SECOND STORYTELLER: "Once upon a time a certain King seized upon all the corn in his country. He had it stored in a strong granary. Then came a swarm of locusts over the land. Soon they found a crack in the south side of the granary. Now the crack was just large enough for one locust to pass through at a time. So one locust went in and carried away a grain of corn. Then another locust went in and carried away a grain of corn. Then another locust went in and carried away a grain of corn. Then—"

27   KING [*interrupting*]: Yes, yes! Now go on with the story.

28   SECOND STORYTELLER: The story shall go on, O King! "Then another locust went in and carried away another grain of corn. Then another locust—"

29   KING [*interrupting*]: I tell you to go on with the story!

30   SECOND STORYTELLER: I obey, great King. "Then another locust went in and carried away another grain of corn. Then another—"

31   KING: The story! The story, I tell you!

32   SECOND STORYTELLER: This is the story, O King! "Then another locust went in and carried away another grain of corn. Then—"

33   KING: I cannot stand it! How long will it take the locusts to carry away all the grain?

34   SECOND STORYTELLER: One thousand years, O King! "Then another locust went in and—"

35   KING: Stop! Stop! Take my daughter! Be King after me! Be King now! Anything to stop the locusts!

36   [*The lights go out. The curtain falls. The play is over.*]

1 Which of the following lines from the play gives a stage direction?

   A *Setting: A long time ago in a grand palace.*

   B KING: Throw him out of the palace, guards! Off with his head!

   C [GUARDS *seize* FIRST STORYTELLER.]

   D SECOND STORYTELLER: "Once upon a time a certain King seized upon all the corn in his country."

2 Which information is presented to readers through the dialogue in the play?

   A The King and the Princess sit on cushions.

   B All the events take place a long time ago.

   C The Second Storyteller bows to the King and Princess.

   D The King wants to hear a story that never ends.

3 Decide about how many actors you would need to put on this play. In your answer, describe the cast of characters, the action, and the dialogue that must be performed in the play.

   _____

   _____

   _____

   _____

   _____

✓ **Self Check**   *Go back and see what you can check off on the Self Check on page 159.*

Lesson 21   Part 1: Introduction 👥

Comparing Poems, Plays, and Prose

CCSS
RL.4.5: Explain major differences between poems, drama, and prose, and refer to the structural elements of poems (e.g., verse, rhythm, meter) and drama (e.g., casts of characters, settings, descriptions, dialogue, stage directions) when writing or speaking about a text.

Theme: *Tales of Right and Wrong*

Poetry, **plays** (also called dramas), and **prose** (stories, novels) are forms of literature. You can probably identify the big differences between them—before you even read a word!

Read the cartoon below. Look closely at the sheets of paper on the author's desk.

> Oh, no! All the words have spilled out of my latest works, leaving just traces behind! Now which was which?

Help the author identify his works by writing the words PLAY, STORY, or POEM on the lines beneath each wordless page.

Read the table below to learn more about the major features of the different forms.

Form of Literature	What It Typically Does	Major Features
Poem	describes feelings and ideas or tells stories using rhythm and often rhyme	• verses, also called lines • stanzas (often) • rhyming words (sometimes)
Play	tells a story through dialogue and actions performed by actors	• mostly dialogue • stage directions • descriptions
Prose (story, novel)	tells a story through a narrator who describes events	• paragraphs • dialogue (usually in quotation marks) • chapters (in novels)

When you understand the major differences between poems, plays, and prose, you'll find yourself enjoying them all more than ever.

Read the story about a boy who goes to his sister's concert.

Genre: **Realistic Fiction**

Angie's Solo   *by Lars Gary*

My sister Angie's glee club was putting on their annual show, and the auditorium was packed. When it came time for her solo, Angie put her heart into it and sang away. But I knew what she could really do—and she just wasn't doing it. In fact, she sounded really flat. But the crowd still cheered.

I almost dreaded seeing her after the show. What would I tell her? All I knew was that I didn't want to hurt her feelings. Then the moment arrived.

"Brian!" she said. "What did you think of my solo?"

I didn't hesitate. "It was beautiful!" I said. She beamed, and I knew at that moment how right I was to think that the truth is sometimes wrong.

Explore how to answer this question: *"What are two features of 'Angie's Solo' that show it is a prose story, not a poem or a play?"*

When you need to identify the features of a text, start by asking: What makes this form of text different from other forms of text? In this case: How is prose different than poetry and plays?

The table on page 193 lists features of poetry, drama, and prose. Use the table to identify two features that show "Angie's Solo" is a prose story, not a poem or play.

First feature of "Angie's Solo": _____

Second feature of "Angie's Solo": _____

Now, imagine that the story "Angie's Solo" is part of a long novel called *My Sister the Singer.*

What does a prose novel have that short stories, plays, and poems do not? _____

Most of "Angie's Solo" is about the narrator's inner thoughts and feelings. Given this fact, what would be the challenge of turning "Angie's Solo" into a play to be acted in front of an audience?

_____

_____

_____

Read the poem about a boy who goes to his sister's concert. Use the Close Reading and the Hint to help you answer the questions.

Close Reading

What are some features of "At the Concert"? **Draw a box** around a stanza and write *stanza* next to it. **Underline** a verse and write *verse* next to it. Finally, **circle** two words that rhyme.

Genre: **Narrative Poem**

At the Concert   *by Lars Gary*

When my sister sang her solo,
I thought it sounded awfully flat.
But I didn't want to hurt her feelings,
So I could hardly tell her that.

5   So later when she asked me
What I thought about her song,
I told her, *It was beautiful,*
Because that night the truth felt wrong.

Hint

Think about features of poems, plays, and prose. Use the table on page 193 to help you.

Answer the questions below.

"Angie's Solo" and "At the Concert" are different forms of literature, but they tell the same story.

What form of literature is "At the Concert"? _____

What are two ways in which "At the Concert" tells the story differently than "Angie's Solo" does? Refer to details from both "At the Concert" and "Angie's Solo" in your answer.

_____

_____

_____

_____

✎ **Show Your Thinking** _____

 Look at line 7 of "At the Concert." Imagine the phrase *It was beautiful* is put into quotation marks. Would that turn "At the Concert" from a poem into a prose story? Talk your answer over with your partner.

Read the play on this page and folktale on the next page. Use the Study Buddies and the Close Reading to guide your reading.

What type of passage is this? Features such as stage directions tell me this is a play. Realizing this is a play will help me picture in my mind what I'm reading.

Close Reading

How does the play tell you about the setting? **Underline** details in the first few lines that tell you where and when the action occurs.

How many actors do you need to perform this play? **Draw a box** around the cast of characters.

The Sound of Money   *based on a Turkish folktale*

1   *Cast of Characters: A* TRAVELER, *an* INNKEEPER, *the* TOWN JUDGE

2   *Setting: Outside a country inn in Turkey, a very long time ago*

3   [*A poor* TRAVELER *stops outside a country inn. The* INNKEEPER *stands outside, cooking a large pot of soup over an open fire.*]

4   TRAVELER [*leans over the pot to smell the soup*]: Oh, I am so hungry. And this soup smells so delicious!

5   INNKEEPER [*angrily grabbing the* TRAVELER's *arm*]: Hey, what do you think you're doing, stealing my soup? Why, you rascal!

6   TRAVELER: But, sir, I took no soup. I was only smelling the steam from the pot.

7   [*Just then the* TOWN JUDGE *walks onto stage. He stops to listen to the* INNKEEPER *and the* TRAVELER.]

8   INNKEEPER: I do not give my soup away. You must pay me, this minute. I demand money!

9   TRAVELER [*pulls out his pockets to show they are empty*]: But I have no money. Not a cent, for I am a poor man.

10   TOWN JUDGE: Ah, but I do! [*He reaches into his pocket and pulls out a handful of coins.*]

11   INNKEEPER: I don't care whose money it is, as long as I get paid for my soup!

12   TOWN JUDGE: And I know just the price you deserve. [*He jingles the handful of coins in front of the* INNKEEPER.] For the smell of the soup, you receive only the sound of the money.

This story tells the same events as the play on page 196. I can compare how prose tells events to how a play does it.

Close Reading

How does the story tell you about the setting? **Circle** two words in paragraph 1 that tell you where the action occurs.

Does a story always use quotation marks to tell what a character says? In paragraph 1, look for and **underline** a sentence that tells what a character says but doesn't use quotation marks.

The Sound of Money   *a Turkish folktale*

1   A beggar was given a piece of bread, but nothing to put on it. Hoping to get something to go with his bread, he went to a nearby inn and asked for a handout. The innkeeper turned him away with nothing, but the beggar sneaked into the kitchen where he saw a large pot of soup cooking over the fire. He held his piece of bread over the steaming pot, hoping to thus capture a bit of flavor from the good-smelling vapor. Suddenly the innkeeper seized him by the arm and angrily accused him of stealing soup.

2   "I took no soup," said the beggar. "I was only smelling the vapor."

3   "Then you must pay for the smell," answered the innkeeper. The poor beggar had no money, so the angry innkeeper dragged him before the qadi[1].

4   Now Nasreddin Hodja was at that time serving as qadi, and he heard the innkeeper's complaint and the beggar's explanation.

5   "So you demand payment for the smell of your soup?" summarized the Hodja after the hearing.

6   "Yes!" insisted the innkeeper.

7   "Then I myself will pay you," said the Hodja, "and I will pay for the smell of your soup with the sound of money."

8   Thus saying, the Hodja drew two coins from his pocket, rang them together loudly, put them back into his pocket, and sent the beggar and the innkeeper each on his own way.

[1] **Qadi:** judge

Hints

What is a feature that plays and stories share?

The writer of a play has to describe the setting both early and quickly. A writer of a story has more freedom about when and how to describe the setting.

Keep in mind who needs to use the script of a play. This will help you explain what each feature needs to do.

Use the Hints to help you answer the questions.

1 What is one way in which the play and the story are alike?

   A   The thoughts of some characters are written out.

   B   Stage directions explain the action.

   C   A cast of characters is provided.

   D   Dialogue is used to help tell the story.

2 Describe one difference between how readers learn about the setting in the play and how they learn about it in the story. Use at least one detail from the play and the story to support your answer.

_____

_____

_____

_____

3 Look at the table below. It contains part of the play and part of the story. These parts tell about the same events.

From the Play	From the Story
INNKEEPER [*angrily grabbing the* TRAVELER's *arm*]: Hey, what do you think you're doing, stealing my soup? Why, you rascal!	Suddenly the innkeeper seized him by the arm and angrily accused him of stealing soup.

Identify the features the play uses to tell events. Then explain why the play must use these features but the story does not.

_____

_____

_____

_____

_____

_____

_____

Read the story and then the play. Then answer the questions that follow.

The Talker

by Ari Washington

1   "Mary, I'm not kidding," Clarisse giggled into the phone. "He was great, and now the whole school knows my brother can dance!"

2   "Clarisse, it's already 7:15. You need to get off the phone and get busy on your homework! You've got a pile of work right next to you on the kitchen table. This is no time to be talking to friends."

3   "Mama, I was just telling Mary about Jerome winning the dance contest," Clarisse said in a wounded tone. "And—"

4   "You can tell her all about it at school tomorrow, but tonight is not the time. I will get up from this chair and take away your phone if I have to."

5   "See you tomorrow, Mary," Clarisse said, sighing.

6   Turning back to her magazine, Clarisse's mother sighed and furrowed her brow. Why did she have to remind Clarisse to quit talking and get down to work? How would things turn out for her if she didn't start getting better grades? All day and night she did nothing but talk, talk, talk. That wasn't a recipe for success.

7   It wasn't a matter of intelligence: Clarisse was as smart as any straight-A student. No, it was a matter of discipline. At this rate, Clarisse would probably wake up one day with no skills and discover herself stuck in a boring job. How would she talk her way out of that kind of unrewarding situation?

8   "Mama," Clarisse announced just then, "I was so excited about Jerome winning the dance contest that I forgot to tell you what else happened today! The Communications Club at school is starting a real AM radio station, and every Tuesday they're going to broadcast a live talk show after school, called 'Talk Time.' So guess who they invited to host it? The biggest little talker you know . . . me!"

The Talker
based on the short story by Ari Washington

CAST OF CHARACTERS

CLARISSE .... a 6th-grade student   **MOTHER** .... Clarisse's mother

1 [*Setting: A bare stage with a kitchen table, four chairs, and a refrigerator.* MOTHER *and* CLARISSE *are at the table.* MOTHER *is reading a magazine.* CLARISSE *is talking on a phone.*]

2 CLARISSE [*into the phone*]: Mary, I'm not kidding! He was great, and now the whole school knows my brother can really dance!

3 MOTHER: Clarisse, it's 7:15. You need to get off the phone and get busy on your homework!

4 CLARISSE [*putting her hand over the phone*]: Mama, I was just telling Mary about Jerome winning the dance contest, and—

5 MOTHER: You can tell her all about it at school tomorrow, but tonight is not the time.

6 CLARISSE [*rolling her eyes and sighing*]: See you tomorrow, Mary. [*hangs up*]

7 MOTHER [*shaking her head*]: Clarisse, all you do all day is talk, talk, talk! Why do I constantly have to remind you to get to work? When are you going to figure out it's the right thing to do?

8 CLARISSE: But Mom, talking isn't so bad, you know. Why, just today at school—

9 MOTHER [*flipping through her magazine, clearly annoyed*]: I mean, really, Clarisse. All that talking is no recipe for success. Nobody ever got anywhere by just talking.

10 CLARISSE: But that's what I'm trying to tell you! Just today—

11 MOTHER [*worried*]: You know, one of these days, you're going to wake up with no skills and have to go to a boring job every day that you hate. That's not right. Don't you want a rewarding career?

12 CLARISSE: Like as a radio talk-show host?

13 MOTHER [*finally looking up from her magazine*]: What?

14 CLARISSE: I've been trying to tell you. The Communications Club at school is starting a real radio station, and every Tuesday they're going to broadcast a live talk show after school, called "Talk Time." So guess who they invited to host it? The biggest little talker you know—me!

15 MOTHER [*laughing*]: Wow! That's great! [*Reaches across to give* CLARISSE *a high-five.*] But you're still going to get serious about your homework. There's no talking your way out of this.

16 [CLARISSE *groans, puts her head down on the table.* MOTHER *smiles, obviously proud. Curtain.*]

1 Look at the table below.

Type of Literature	Major Features of Work
Story of "The Talker"	paragraphs, narration, and dialogue
Play of "The Talker"	?

Which of the following choices correctly completes the table?

A stanzas, dialogue, and meter

B cast of characters, paragraphs, and rhyme

C verse, meter, rhythm

D description, stage directions, and dialogue

2 Part of the play of "The Talker" is shown below.

[*A bare stage with a kitchen table, four chairs, and a refrigerator.* MOTHER *and* CLARISSE *are at the table.* MOTHER *is reading a magazine.* CLARISSE *is talking on a phone.*]

State what feature of the play "The Talker" this part indicates to the reader.

_____

Look back at the story of "The Talker." State how the story gives this same information to the reader.

_____

State why the play and the story present the same information in different ways. Explain your answer.

_____

_____

_____

3   Look at the table below. It contains part of the story and part of the play. These parts tell about the same events.

From the Story	From the Play
At this rate, Clarisse would probably wake up one day with no skills and discover herself stuck in a boring job. How would she talk her way out of that kind of unrewarding situation?	Mother [*worried*]: You know, one of these days, you're going to wake up with no skills and have to go to a boring job every day that you hate. That's not right. Don't you want a rewarding career?

Describe **one** feature of **prose** that the story uses to show what Mother thinks about Clarisse's future.

_____

_____

Now describe **two** features of **drama** that the play uses to show how Mother feels and thinks about Clarisse's future.

Feature one: _____

_____

Feature two: _____

_____

Finally, explain why the **story** and the **play** show Mother's thoughts in different ways.

_____

_____

_____

_____

 **Self Check**   *Go back and see what you can check off on the Self Check on page 159.*

Read the story. Then answer the questions that follow.

The Escape

a story by John Martin

1   Carl picked at the lock of the prison cell he shared with Kasper. He almost had it, he was sure. They didn't have much time before the prince's guards returned for them.

2   The only light in the stone dungeon came from two bad-smelling torches on the walls. His friend Kasper lay groaning on the cold damp floor by his feet.

3   "What a foolish thing we've done," Kasper said, "Did we do the right thing, trying to help that old couple?"

4   "The prince's men were stealing the last of their food," Carl said. "We had to try and help them."

5   "The two of us, with our shovels and hoes, we weren't much of a match for those thugs, were we?" Kasper said, laughing. "But we put up a good fight!" He let out a sharp moan. "But, oh, my leg is hurt bad!"

6   "We've got to get you help," Carl said. "The monks at the monastery will know what to do. But first, we must escape." He picked at the lock a moment more, then smiled and pushed the creaking door open.

7   "I can barely stand, let alone walk," Kasper said. "You might make it alone, but you won't have a chance with me."

8   Carl stood in silence, thinking. *What Kasper said may very well be true. But more than likely, he would not survive here.*

9   "To escape alone would be no escape at all," Carl said firmly. "I'd be a prisoner, trapped and wandering in the labyrinth of my mind if I leave my brave friend behind."

10   Carl raised Kasper up, stooped, and lifted him onto his shoulders. Together they escaped as one into the moonlit night.

Answer Form
1 Ⓐ Ⓑ Ⓒ Ⓓ
2 Ⓐ Ⓑ Ⓒ Ⓓ **Number**
3 Ⓐ Ⓑ Ⓒ Ⓓ **Correct** /3

Answer the questions. Mark your answers to
questions 1–3 on the Answer Form to the right.

1 What does the word "labyrinth" mean as it is used in paragraph 9?

  A castle

  B forest

  C maze

  D city

2 The sentence below is from paragraph 6 of the story.

  He picked at the lock a moment more, then smiled and pushed the creaking door open.

  What element in the text of a play would **most likely** give this information to the reader?

  A stage directions

  B dialogue

  C setting

  D cast of characters

3 How would the story be different if it were told from Kasper's point of view?

  A The reader would feel sad about Kasper's time in prison.

  B The reader would know Kasper's inner thoughts instead of Carl's.

  C The reader would know how Kasper's injury happened.

  D The reader would understand more about Carl's feelings than Kasper's.

Read the play. Then answer the questions that follow.

The Escape

a play by John Martin

CAST OF CHARACTERS

CARL .... A prisoner

KASPER .... A prisoner

1 [*Setting: The dark, underground prison in an evil prince's castle, a long time ago.*]

2 [*Curtain opens on a torch-lit, stone dungeon. Two prisoners, CARL and KASPER, can be seen behind bars. CARL is reaching through the bars, working on a lock. KASPER lies on the floor.*]

3 KASPER: What a foolish thing we've done, to land ourselves here, in the prince's dungeon. Did we do the right thing, Carl, trying to help that old couple?

4 CARL: The prince's men were stealing the last of their food. Those poor people are already near starving, and almost everything they grow goes to the castle. We had to try and help them.

5 KASPER: The two of us, with our shovels and hoes, we weren't much of a match for armed guards, were we? But we put up a fight! [*He groans and holds his leg.*] Oh, but I am hurt bad!

6 CARL: Your leg will heal, but we've got to get you help. The monks at the monastery will know what to do. But first, we must escape. [*He picks at the lock some more.*] I think I've almost got it. There! [*He pulls the lock off and opens their cell door. He steps out and looks both ways.*]

7 KASPER [*pulls himself up from the floor, groaning*]: Carl, you must go alone. I can barely stand, let alone walk. You can make it on your own, but you won't have a chance with me.

8 CARL [*thinking*]: What you say may be true. If I escaped, I might get a message to King Halberd. If he hears what the Prince and his men have been doing, his people might help you. He's a good man, and nothing like his wicked son.

9 KASPER: Then go, Carl. Leave while you can. Run!

10 CARL [*reaching for the door, then stopping and straightening his back*]: I can't do this without you, Kasper. To escape alone would be no escape at all. I'd be a prisoner in the labyrinth of my mind if I left you, my brave friend, behind.

11 [CARL *stoops and lifts* KASPER *onto his shoulders. They exit the stage. The lights go down on the open cell door.*]

Answer Form

4 Ⓐ Ⓑ Ⓒ Ⓓ
5 Ⓐ Ⓑ Ⓒ Ⓓ
6 Ⓐ Ⓑ Ⓒ Ⓓ

Number Correct /3

4 Read the following sentence from the play of "The Escape."

> He's a good man, and nothing like his wicked son.

What does the word "wicked" mean as it is used in the sentence?

A childish

B evil

C dangerous

D foolish

5 Below is a line from the play of "The Escape."

> KASPER [*pulls himself up from the floor, groaning*]: Carl, you must go alone.

What two features of a play does this line include?

A cast of characters and stage directions

B setting and dialogue

C cast of characters and setting

D stage directions and dialogue

6 Imagine that the playwright wanted parts of the play of "The Escape" to have a first-person narrator. How could the playwright **best** do this?

A Kasper could speak directly to the audience.

B Carl could tell Kasper more about the monks at the monastery.

C Kasper could say more about what happened to the old couple.

D Carl could describe in greater detail what the guards did.

Read the poem. Then answer the questions that follow.

The Escape

a poem by John Martin

Two strong and brave men were locked in a cell
For fighting the Prince and his ne'er-do-well men.
One man was injured, the other stayed well,
But both swore they'd rise up and do it again.

The well man, he picked at the lock of the door,
And then faced a choice—leave his sick friend behind?
The well man, he knew that would lead, ever more
To making a cage of his own guilty mind.

---

7 What is the meaning of "guilty" as it is used in the last line of the poem?

A troubled

B excited

C curious

D honest

Answer Form

7 Ⓐ Ⓑ Ⓒ Ⓓ **Number Correct** / 1

---

8 How does the organization of the poem into stanzas help the reader understand its meaning? Include examples to support your answer.

_____

_____

_____

_____

9 The box below lists six features related to stories, plays, and poems.

TERMS
stanzas
meter
paragraphs
stage directions
dialogue in quotes
cast of characters

Complete the table below by writing each feature in the correct column. Write down each feature only once.

Story	Play	Poem

10 Both the story and the poem of "The Escape" tell how Carl and Kasper came to be in prison. Compare how the story and the poem present this event. Refer to at least one feature of a story and one feature of a play in your answer.

_____

_____

_____

_____

_____

_____

Performance Task—Extended Response

11 The table below contains parts of the story and the play. These parts both show Carl reaching his decision to take Kasper with him.

From the Story	From the Play
Carl stood in silence, thinking. *What Kasper said may very well be true. But more than likely, he would not survive here.*	Carl [*reaching for the door, then stopping and straightening his back*]: I can't do this without you, Kasper.

Compare how the story and the play show Carl's decision. Why do the story and the play show Carl's decision in such different ways? Use details from both the story and the play to support your answer.

In your answer, be sure to include
• what features the story uses to show the decision
• what features the play uses to show the decision
• why the story and the play showed the decision as they did
• details from both the story and the play to support your answer

Check your writing for correct spelling, grammar, capitalization, and punctuation.

_____

_____

_____

_____

_____

_____

How are good readers like smart shoppers? Smart shoppers look for facts before they buy a product. For example, imagine you want new sneakers. A smart shopper would look at a magazine or website to see the new styles. You'd find out what others think about the best sneakers. Then, you'd go to a store and ask the salespeople what they think. Finally, you'd try on more than one pair to see how they feel and look. In the same way, when good readers need to learn about a topic, they gather **knowledge** and **ideas** from different

sources. They identify an author's points and figure out if those points are well supported. They put together, or **integrate**, facts from those sources to fully understand a topic.

In this unit, you'll read information in visual displays to help you better understand a text. You'll learn how an author uses reasons and evidence to support a point. You'll read and combine information from two sources about a topic. Good readers, like smart shoppers, do a lot of work—but what you get at the end is totally worth it.

✓ Self Check

Before starting this unit, check off the skills you know below. As you complete each lesson, see how many more you can check off!

I know how to:	Before this unit	After this unit
read and understand information presented in charts, graphs, diagrams, and time lines.	☐	☐
explain how the information in charts, graphs, diagrams, and time lines helps me better understand a text.	☐	☐
explain how authors use reasons and evidence to support their points.	☐	☐
combine information from two texts when writing about a single topic.	☐	☐

Lesson 22   Part 1: Introduction 👥
Interpreting Visual Information

CCSS
RI.4.7: Interpret information presented visually, orally, or quantitatively (e.g., in charts, graphs, diagrams, time lines . . .) and explain how the information contributes to an understanding of the text in which it appears.

Theme: *Exploring the Seas*

You've probably read stories that had pictures of characters and places. Those pictures helped you understand the story in ways that words alone could not. Charts, graphs, diagrams, and time lines are like pictures for informational texts. Each of these **visual displays** presents information in ways that sentences and paragraphs alone do not.

Read the text, then look at the bar graph. As you look at the graph, think about how the information it shows adds to what the text is telling you.

A few months ago, I helped my science teacher set up a fish tank. The tank has three types of fish. We put in just two of the largest type of fish and many of the smaller types of fish. The tank is large enough to follow this rule: Each fish needs about one gallon of water to be healthy.

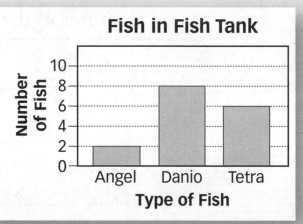

Now look at the table. It brings together facts from the text and the graph.

What the Text Says	What the Graph Shows
"The tank has three types of fish."	The three types of fish are angel, danio, and tetra.
"We put in just two of the largest type of fish . . . ."	There are only two angel fish, so angel fish must be the largest type of fish.
"Each fish needs about one gallon of water to be healthy."	There are two angel fish, eight danios, and six tetras. This is 16 fish, so the tank holds at least 16 gallons of water.

Reading the text, looking at the graph, and then putting together the information in the text and the graph gives you a pretty good idea of what that fish tank looks like.

Most informational text you read will have visual displays. Studying and understanding what visual displays say will bring the text more fully to life.

Read the start of a science passage about features on the ocean floor.

Genre: **Science**

Features of the Ocean Floor   *by Connie Rather*

Picture this: You're in a submarine right next to a continent. Looking down, you see a part of the ocean floor called the **continental shelf**. Now, head out to sea. The ocean floor drops away as the **continental slope**. You might pass through a range of **seamounts**, or volcanoes rising from the ocean floor. In time, you'll reach the **abyssal plain**, a dark realm with deep valleys called **trenches**. Finally, you might encounter long, snakelike **ocean ridges** that rise from the ocean floor and wrap themselves around the planet.

Features of the Ocean Floor

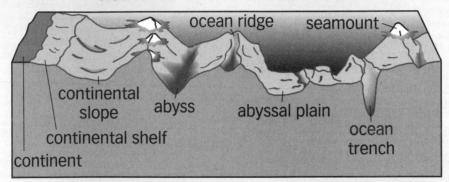

(continued)

Explore how to answer this question: *"The passage says that seamounts and ocean ridges both rise from the ocean floor. What are some differences between seamounts and ocean ridges that the passage does not describe?"*

On the diagram, find the features labeled "ocean ridge" and "seamount." Look for differences.

One difference is that an ocean ridge has a valley in its middle. The seamount does not.

Look for one more difference between the ocean ridge and the seamount. Describe it below.

_____

_____

_____

The diagram gives you information about the two features that the passage does not.

Continue reading the science text about the ocean floor. Use the Close Reading and Hint to help you answer the question.

Close Reading

Graphs often provide information that words alone do not. **Circle** a part of the graph that gives you information the sentences do not.

(continued from page 214)

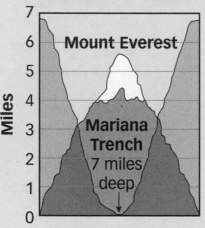

Highest and Deepest Places on Earth

The deepest ocean trench in the world is the Mariana Trench in the Pacific. It is one of the most difficult places to reach on Earth. It is so deep that if Mount Everest, one of the tallest mountains in the world, were picked up and put at the bottom of the trench, the mountain would still be covered with water!

Hint

The passage compares the height and depth of the features, but it does not mention miles.

Circle the correct answer.

What information do you learn from the graph about the Mariana Trench and Mount Everest that you cannot learn from the passage?

A the names of the trench and the mountain

B the depth of the trench and the height of the mountain

C the fact that the mountain is located inside the trench

D the difficulty that explorers have in reaching both features

✎ Show Your Thinking

Explain why it is important to look at diagrams, graphs, and other visual displays that come with any passages that you read.

_____

_____

 Use the graph to figure out how much deeper the Mariana Trench is than Mount Everest is tall.

Read the science passage. Use the Study Buddy and the Close Reading to guide your reading.

I see a diagram at the bottom of the passage. It must be important! After I read each paragraph, I'll look at the diagram to see if it gives me more information about what I just read.

Close Reading

The text describes the depth of each zone. How does the diagram help you understand where these zones are compared to each other?

Diagrams often give information that the text does not. **Circle** one fact in the diagram that is not in the text.

Genre: **Science**

Going Down, Down, Down   *by Justin Oh*

1   The ocean has three main zones. These zones are distinguished by the amount of sunlight they receive.

2   In the **sunlight zone,** the sun's rays penetrate from the surface to a depth of 650 feet. The light lets plants grow here, and these plants provide food for animals. Here you will find sea mammals and schools of fish.

3   The **twilight zone** stretches from 650 feet to 3,300 feet below the ocean surface. There is almost no sunlight, so no plants grow. Animals that live here wait for dead plants and animals to drift down from the sunlit zone. The animals here have ways of surviving difficult conditions. Many can produce their own light, which helps them search for food.

4   Below 3,300 feet, the **midnight zone** lies in complete darkness. There is very little food, the water is cold, and the water pressure is enormous. Some animals at this level are soft, so the pressure doesn't affect them as much. Many are blind or have no eyes, but they can feel the smallest movement of food that might brush up against them.

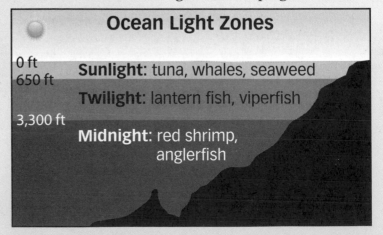

Ocean Light Zones

0 ft
650 ft
Sunlight: tuna, whales, seaweed

Twilight: lantern fish, viperfish

3,300 ft

Midnight: red shrimp, anglerfish

Hints

The text tells you which zone has animals with soft bodies and no eyes. The diagram lists some animals that live in that zone. You can put that information together.

Make sure your choice is related to the depths of the three zones.

It's true that the passage refers to plants and animals. But how specific does the passage get about these life-forms? Where can you find more specific information?

Use the Hints on this page to help you answer the questions.

1 Which ocean animals listed in the diagram are most likely to live among creatures that have soft bodies and no eyes?

 A red shrimp and anglerfish

 B viperfish and lantern fish

 C tuna and whales

 D red shrimp and tuna

2 The passage describes where the sunlight, twilight, and midnight zones begin and end. How does the diagram help the reader better understand this description of the three zones?

 A It names some animals that live in those zones.

 B It shows the amount of light each zone gets.

 C It compares where each zone is relative to the other zones.

 D It identifies the location of each zone along the shoreline.

3 Describe at least one type of information you can find in the diagram that the passage does not give you. Use at least one detail from both the passage and the diagram to support your answer.

_____

_____

_____

_____

_____

_____

_____

_____

_____

Read the science passage. Then answer the questions that follow.

Voyage to the Bottom of the Sea

by Martine Costi

1   On January 23, 1960, six-foot waves rocked the surface seven miles above the Mariana Trench in the Pacific Ocean. Carefully, Jacques Piccard and Donald Walsh rowed a small rubber boat toward the *Trieste*. This craft would soon take them seven miles down to the deepest part of the ocean's floor.

2   No one had ever explored the Mariana Trench before. It was so deep that the weight of the miles of water above it would crush most crafts. The *Trieste* was built to withstand such pressure, however, so the men inside should be safe on their underwater journey. During the descent, the men on the *Trieste* would communicate by radio with the surface.

Diagram of the *Trieste*

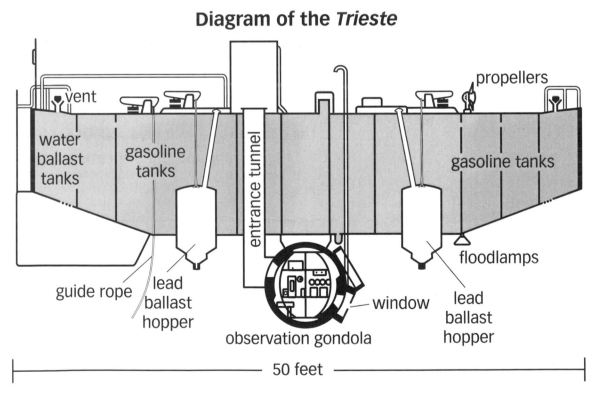

3   Shortly after 8:00 A.M., Piccard and Walsh sat jammed in the *Trieste*'s observation gondola. The space was so small that they could barely move, but they were ready. Water from the ocean filled the water ballast tanks. Slowly, the *Trieste* began traveling down to the trench.

4   At 340 feet, Piccard released gasoline from the tanks, letting water fill them instead. Water weighs more than gasoline, so this made the craft sink farther into the darkness.

5   An hour later and a mile farther down, the men saw plankton. These are tiny ocean creatures that glow in specks of yellowish green. Two hours later, they were more than five miles down, and there was no sign of life.

6   A little past noon, they were about a half-mile from the bottom. Then they heard a small explosion. Tension flooded the observation gondola, but nothing seemed wrong, so they agreed to keep going. Just before one o'clock, they reached the bottom of the Mariana Trench. They had landed where no other human had ever been.

7   They flashed lights and saw a flat, white fish about a foot long that Piccard described as a sole. Little red shrimp swam in front of their window. Both discoveries were ground breaking. Now humans knew that animals lived on the deepest part of the ocean floor.

8   Then the men turned on an inside light. Piccard spotted the cause of the earlier noise— it was a cracked window. Now he became more worried about their safety. Piccard released 800 pounds of lead pellets from the ballast chamber. Releasing this weight caused the *Trieste* to move upwards. Piccard and Walsh could hear people speaking on the radio, but for some reason no one could hear them speaking back.

9   At 5:00 P.M., the *Trieste* emerged. No one had heard Piccard on the wireless for hours, so the people above did not know what to expect. The crews on both ships watched breathlessly for movement from the *Trieste*. They waited for fifteen long minutes. Then suddenly, the two men emerged unharmed. They had traveled to the deepest part of the ocean and made history.

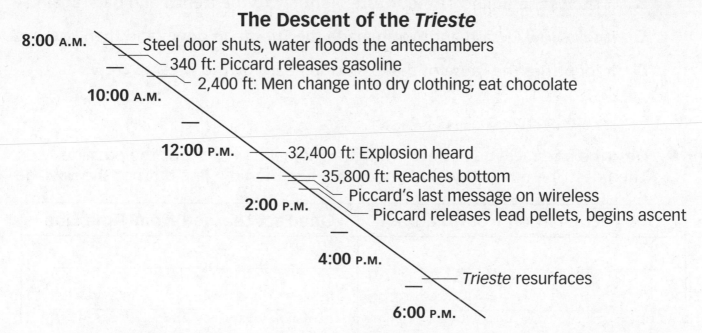

The Descent of the *Trieste*

8:00 A.M. — Steel door shuts, water floods the antechambers
— 340 ft: Piccard releases gasoline
— 2,400 ft: Men change into dry clothing; eat chocolate

10:00 A.M. —

12:00 P.M. — 32,400 ft: Explosion heard
— 35,800 ft: Reaches bottom
— Piccard's last message on wireless
2:00 P.M. — Piccard releases lead pellets, begins ascent
—

4:00 P.M.
— *Trieste* resurfaces

6:00 P.M.

1   The *Trieste* used tanks and hoppers to complete its journey. What does the diagram show that helps you understand these features of the *Trieste*?

   A   It shows you the locations and sizes of the tanks and hoppers compared with the observation gondola in which the men were sitting.

   B   It tells you the specific amounts of water, gasoline, and lead pellets needed to travel to the Mariana Trench and back again.

   C   It shows you how the tanks and the hoppers worked to bring in the water and then get rid of the gasoline and the lead pellets.

   D   It tells you why the journey to the Mariana Trench could not have been completed without the tanks and the hoppers.

2   What information does the time line include that helps the reader understand Piccard and Walsh's journey to the Mariana Trench?

   A   It describes the radio conversations between the *Trieste* and the surface.

   B   It shows the timing of the *Trieste*'s journey to the trench and back again.

   C   It tells how Piccard and Walsh made the *Trieste* go down and then back up.

   D   It identifies the cause of the explosion heard by the *Trieste*'s crew.

3   Describe one fact you learned from just the diagram but not the passage. Then describe one fact you learned from just the time line but not the passage.

One Fact Learned from Diagram	One Fact Learned from Time Line

✓ **Self Check**   *Go back and see what you can check off on the Self Check on page 211.*

Lesson 23 Part 1: Introduction 👥

Explaining an Author's Reasons and Evidence

CCSS
RI.4.8: Explain how an author uses reasons and evidence to support particular points in a text.

Theme: *Exploring Space*

Imagine that it's the year 2450. Humans now live on the Moon. But some things don't change: Most kids want to have pets. And there's something else that hasn't changed. The grown-ups usually have to be convinced that a pet is a good idea. Convincing anyone about a **point** (a claim) takes good **reasons** (ideas) and **evidence** (facts).

Look at the pictures below. Think about how each child is asking for a pet.

Which child do you think is more likely to get a pet? Explain why you think this.

_____

_____

Both children want a pet, but the girl calmly gives reasons and facts to back up her point. The chart below shows her point, one reason, and two facts she gives.

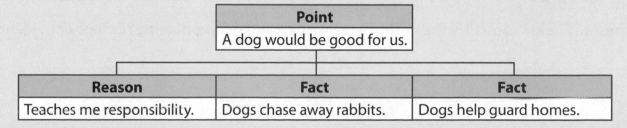

Point		
A dog would be good for us.		

Reason	Fact	Fact
Teaches me responsibility.	Dogs chase away rabbits.	Dogs help guard homes.

Authors who make points should back them up with good reasons and solid evidence. Studying how authors use reasons and evidence can give you ideas for backing up your own points—for example, if you want to convince your family to get a new pet.

Read the first paragraph of an essay that discusses whether people should explore space.

Genre: **Persuasive Essay**

Should We Explore Space? Absolutely!   by Marc Lucas

Exploring space is one of the most important things the United States can do. But why? For one reason, the work of getting people and machines into space leads to new technologies. Some of these new technologies then become available to everyone and improves their lives. Do you need examples? Then try these: Because of the space program of the 1960s and 1970s, we have digital clocks, laser surgery, and instant foods. And these new technologies have broader effects on society. They help create new businesses, which then make new jobs, a richer population, and a stronger economy.

(continued)

Explore how to answer this question: *"Identify the main point the author makes in this paragraph. What reasons or evidence does the author use to support this point?"*

Use the chart to identify the author's main point, reasons, and evidence. Fill in the empty boxes.

Main Point
Humans should explore space.

Reason or Evidence	Reason or Evidence	Reason or Evidence
Space exploration makes new technologies for people.	_____ _____ _____ _____.	_____ _____ _____ _____.

On the lines below, describe the author's main point and his supporting reasons or evidence.

_____

_____

_____

_____

Continue reading the essay about exploring space. Use the Close Reading and the Hint to help you answer the question.

Close Reading

A *reason* gives an answer to a question that begins with "why." *Evidence* is a fact. **Underline** a reason for why humans should explore space. Then **circle** any information that seems like a fact.

(continued from page 222)

But there is a second and more important reason for exploring space, and it has nothing to do with money. It's called the need to discover. Human beings are naturally curious. We want to know what's out there. If it's the top of a mountain, or across a river, or at the bottom of the sea, we want to see it and touch it.

Humans are also competitive—we want to be both the first *and* the best at what we do. When the Soviet Union put the first human in space in 1961, Americans didn't just sit and watch. The United States surged ahead with a space program and eight years later put the first person on the Moon.

Hint

Which choice gives you evidence (a fact) supporting the author's point that humans are competitive?

Circle the correct answer.

What sentence gives the most specific evidence for the author's point that humans are competitive?

A "Human beings are naturally curious."

B "If it's the top of a mountain, or across a river, or at the bottom of the sea, we want to see it and touch it."

C "Humans are also competitive—we want to be both the first *and* the best at what we do."

D "The United States surged ahead with a space program and eight years later put the first person on the Moon."

✎ Show Your Thinking

Look at the answer you chose above. Explain why you think that choice provided the most specific evidence for the author's point that humans are competitive.

_____

_____

_____

Read the essay about settling on the Moon. Use the Study Buddy and the Close Reading to guide your reading.

Genre: **Persuasive Essay**

I see that the title of this passage is a question. I bet the author will use the passage to answer this question. I'll look for any reasons and evidence the author uses in her answer.

Close Reading

Does the author admit that settling on the Moon might be fun? **Underline** anything that suggests this.

The author feels that regolith is a bigger problem than the lack of air and water. **Circle** any evidence you find of regolith's dangers.

Should We Settle the Moon?   *by Jo Newbold*

1   Whenever people say "Let's shoot for the moon!," they mean that anything is possible. So, when people think of space exploration, a colony on the Moon seems like the next step. The views from the Moon would be spectacular, and being a "Moontonian" would be exciting. But is it feasible?

2   Let's start with the Moon's surface, which is not an easy place for life to thrive. There is little atmosphere, so all air would have to be brought from Earth. The lack of atmosphere causes temperatures to vary greatly, from 232°F during the day to –315°F at night. And then there's the radiation. Without a thick, Earth-like atmosphere to filter the sun's rays, radiation would sicken any colonists.

3   And what about water? True, there is ice below the Moon's surface. If astronauts can mine that ice, they can melt it and use it to make oxygen and rocket fuel. But if the ice is unreachable, all water would have to be carted up to the Moon—a cumbersome and unworkable task.

4   But the biggest obstacle to living on the Moon is the regolith. Regolith is a layer of fine, stone dust. It covers almost the entire surface and sticks to everything. It can gum up a spacesuit, jam an engine, and ruin machines. Worst of all, if we couldn't find a way to keep it out of the colony, it would destroy the lungs of everyone living there.

5   So, will we ever have a Moon colony? Never say never, but today our technology does not make the idea practical.

Hints

Use the Hints on this page to help you answer the questions.

Which choice makes you think, "Oh, now I have a real fact that tells why the Moon is dangerous"?

1 The author thinks that colonizing the Moon is a bad idea because the environment is too dangerous. Which sentence has evidence supporting this point?

A "Let's start with the Moon's surface, which is not an easy place for life to thrive."

B "Without a thick, Earth-like atmosphere to filter the sun's rays, radiation would sicken any colonists."

C "If astronauts can mine that ice, they can melt it and use it to make oxygen and rocket fuel."

D "Never say never, but today our technology does not make the idea practical."

Although the author thinks that humans are not ready to settle the Moon, she knows that a lot of people think it would be fun.

2 Read the sentence below.

The views from the Moon would be spectacular, and being a "Moontonian" would be exciting.

Why does the author most likely say this?

A to declare that humans are ready to colonize the Moon

B to convince people to support space exploration

C to claim that the adventure of space travel outweighs its risks

D to admit that colonizing the Moon is an appealing idea

The author supports her point about the dangers of regolith with some facts. What facts does she give?

3 Describe two types of evidence the author gives to support her point that regolith would make living on the Moon difficult.

_____

_____

_____

_____

_____

Read the science article. Then answer the questions that follow.

from "Mapping Mars: Robots on the Red Planet"

by Janelle Bitikofer, Appleseeds

1   On January 3, 2004, a package dropped out of space. It opened a parachute and landed on the planet Mars. It had left Earth seven months earlier and traveled more than 300 million miles. It bounced 28 times before finally coming to a stop. Then the package opened and out rolled a six-legged rover robot named *Spirit.*

2   In the Mission Control room, scientists jumped up and down with excitement. Humans can't travel to Mars yet. It is too far and too cold, and there's not enough oxygen to breathe. So scientists built and sent *Spirit* and her twin sister, *Opportunity*, to Mars to learn more about the Red Planet.

3   *Spirit* and *Opportunity* are working hard to keep track of the temperature, the weather, and the atmosphere on Mars. They're taking a close look at the dirt and rocks. *Spirit*, *Opportunity*, and other spacecraft orbiting Mars have also taken many photos. Using these special radar images, scientists are making a detailed topographic map of the planet. The type of map shows mountains, valleys, and other geographical features. This same kind of technology was used on the Shuttle *Endeavor* to take images of Earth. Scientists have used these images to create the most detailed topographic map of our home planet ever made.

> **Planetary Rust Belt**
> Scientists believe that Mars is red because it's rusty! There's a lot of iron on Mars, and when iron comes into contact with water (which Mars used to have) and oxygen (which it still has), it rusts.

4   One amazing thing that the Mars photos have shown us are dried-up lakebeds. The rovers have also found round rocks that look like they were carved by water. For scientist Virginia Gulick and her friends at NASA, this is exciting news. "One thing we know from studying Earth is that wherever there is water, there is life," she says. That means there may have been life on Mars long ago. But there isn't any now. And the water is gone, too. So what happened?

5   NASA scientists want to find out. They plan to send other robots and spacecraft to Mars every two years. The maps that are being made now might one day help the new robots find their way around the mountains and valleys of Mars.

Cameras on Mars Exploration Rover *Spirit* took 470 images of the Mars landscape. NASA calls the area the "Columbia Hills." Then it took weeks to send the data back to Earth and weeks to put together one panoramic photograph electronically.

Answer the questions. Mark your answers to questions 1–3 on the Answer Form to the right.

Answer Form

1 Ⓐ Ⓑ Ⓒ Ⓓ

2 Ⓐ Ⓑ Ⓒ Ⓓ   **Number** ⁄3

3 Ⓐ Ⓑ Ⓒ Ⓓ   **Correct**

1   Read the following sentences from the passage.

> *Spirit*, *Opportunity*, and other spacecraft orbiting Mars have also taken many photos. Using these special radar images, scientists are making a detailed topographic map of the planet. The type of map shows mountains, valleys, and other geographical features. This same kind of technology was used on the Shuttle *Endeavor* to take images of Earth. Scientists have used these images to create the most detailed topographic map of our home planet ever made.

The author uses these sentences as evidence to support which of the following points?

A   Mars is a lot like Earth because both planets have supported life.

B   The maps now being created will help scientists explore Mars in the future.

C   *Spirit* and *Opportunity* are robots that can go to places humans can't go.

D   Scientists believe that there may have been water on Mars long ago.

2   What reason does the author give to support her point that humans can't yet travel to Mars?

    A   The robots sent to explore Mars do not need oxygen to survive.

    B   It's too hard to keep track of the weather and temperature on Mars.

    C   Mars is too far away, too cold, and has too little oxygen.

    D   The water on Mars has been gone for a long time, and no one knows why.

3   Look at the table below.

Point	Evidence Supporting the Point
Scientists think there may have once been water on Mars.	?

Which of the following sentences should replace the question mark in the box?

    A   All of the water that once existed on Mars is now gone.

    B   Scientists are using robots to make a detailed map of the surface of Mars.

    C   Mars rover photographs show what appear to be dried-up lakebeds.

    D   Where there is water, there exists the possibility of life.

4   The author states that Mars might once have held life. Write a paragraph that explains what information in the article supports this idea. Use at least **two** details from the article in your answer.

_____

_____

_____

_____

✓ **Self Check**   *Go back and see what you can check off on the Self Check on page 211.*

Integrating Information from Two Sources

CCSS

RI.4.9: Integrate information from two texts on the same topic in order to write or speak about the subject knowledgeably.

Theme: *Exploring the Land*

Imagine that your teacher gives you this social-studies assignment:

- First, pick an island where people live. You will learn how they came to live there.

- Then, find two websites about the history of the island and its people.

- In a two-column table, write down three facts from each site about the history of people on that island. The table helps you remember where you found the facts.

- Finally, write a paragraph that puts together the facts from the two websites.

You pick Tasmania—you like how the name sounds—and find two websites about it. You quickly see that the sites describe very different times in Tasmania's long history.

Read the table below. Consider how you might combine the facts in a paragraph.

www.tas–prehistory.org	www.modern–tas.org
• Tasmania and Australia used to be connected as a single large island. • Humans walked to the land that would become Tasmania about 30,000 years ago. • 10,000 years ago, the ocean split Tasmania and Australia. People stayed on the island.	• In 1642, a Dutch sailor discovered Tasmania and its people. • In 1794, the French built the first European-style town on Tasmania. • In 1856, European nations all agreed to call the island "Tasmania."

So, you've found your facts. It's time to combine them in a paragraph—like this one.

A Short Report on the Long History of People in Tasmania

About 30,000 years ago, Australia and the land that would become Tasmania were one land mass. The first people who came to Tasmania were able to walk there. Then, about 10,000 years ago, the ocean split Tasmania from Australia, but people remained on the new island. Europeans discovered the island and its people in 1642, built the first European-style town in 1794, and named the island "Tasmania" in 1856.

Finding and combining information from two sources is a great skill to practice. The more reading you do, the more information you'll gather, and the more information you gather, the more knowledgeable you'll be.

Read the following history text about the explorer Henry Hudson and his voyage in 1607.

Genre: **History**

Henry Hudson

by Edward R. Shaw, Explorers and Discoverers

Henry Hudson was one of the best sea captains in all England. He loved the ocean, and he did not know the word "fear."

In 1607 a company of London merchants sent him to look for a northwest passage to China. If such a passage could be found, the journey to China would be much shorter than by the overland route then used. It would take less time to sail around the earth near the pole than to sail around the earth near the equator. Besides, every one who had attempted to reach China by sailing west had reached, instead, that long coast of the New World, through which but one opening had ever been found. The route through this opening, the Strait of Magellan, had been proved by its discoverer, Ferdinand Magellan, to be too long for use in commerce, so traders were trying hard to find a northwest passage.

Explore how to answer these questions: *"What was Henry Hudson's mission? Why was the mission important?"*

First, describe Hudson's mission, using details from the passage.

Henry Hudson's mission in 1607 was to _____

_____.

Who sent Henry Hudson on his mission? _____

_____

Now, explain why Hudson's mission was important. As you reread the passage, ask yourself: "What details tell me why Henry Hudson's mission was so important?"

According to the passage, Henry Hudson's mission was important because _____

_____

_____

_____.

Now read a history text about Hudson's voyage in 1609. Use the Close Reading and the Hint to help you answer the question.

Genre: **History**

The Coming of the Dutch   *by John McMaster*

There came in 1609 an intruder in the form of a little Dutch ship called the *Half-Moon*. The Dutch East India Company had fitted her out and sent Captain Henry Hudson in her to seek a northeasterly passage to China. Driven back by ice in his attempt to sail north of Europe, Hudson turned westward, and came at last to Delaware Bay. Up this the *Half-Moon* went a little way, but, grounding on the shoals, Hudson turned about, followed the coast northward, and sailed up the river now called by his name. He went as far as the site of Albany; then, finding that the Hudson was not a passage through the continent, he returned to Europe.

Close Reading

This passage is also about Henry Hudson, but read it carefully— which voyage is it describing? **Circle** the dates in both passages. Then **underline** facts about who sent Hudson on each mission.

Hint

Look at the first passage again. You underlined information about who sent Hudson on this voyage. Now look for words that tell why they sent him. **Draw a box** around these words.

Answer the question below.

Why did English and Dutch businesses send Henry Hudson on his voyages? Use at least one detail from each passage in your answer.

_____

_____

_____

_____

_____

_____

Show Your Thinking

 Discuss with a partner the difference between describing events and explaining events. Use details from "Henry Hudson" and "The Coming of the Dutch" to talk about the difference.

Read these science passages about the continent of Antarctica. Use the Study Buddy and the Close Reading to guide your reading.

Genre: **Science**

Here are two passages about Antarctica. After I read the second passage, I'll ask myself, "What new information did I learn about Antarctica?" Then, I'll say in my own words what I learned from both passages.

Close Reading

The first passage describes Antarctica's climate, including changes in sunlight over the year. The second passage tells about how animals survive in Antarctica, including how they react to changes in sunlight. **Underline** a sentence in *each* passage that tells about changes in sunlight over the year in Antarctica.

A Desert of Ice   *by Tam Tohoku*

1   Antarctica is the most forbidding continent in the world. Home of the South Pole, it exists beneath a five-kilometer sheet of ice. It is also the coldest continent. During its warmest month, January, the average high temperature is –28°C. A cruel –89.2°C was recorded one August. The sun shines continuously from mid-September to mid-March, then disappears for the other half of the year. And while we normally think of deserts as hot, sandy places, Antarctica also qualifies as one. It gets just 2.5 to 5 centimeters of precipitation a year. It is truly a land of extremes.

Antarctica's Life   *by Morgan Minier*

1   The only animals that live on land in Antarctica year-round are a handful of insects and bugs. These year-round dwellers become inactive during the cold, dark winters, but they wake when daylight arrives and the air warms. The largest of these animals is a midge, a wingless insect that looks like a fly. Tiny ticks also live in Antarctica, and they feed on sea birds like penguins. Other year-round buggy residents of Antarctica include mites, lice, and springtails.

2   So what about penguins and seals, the animals normally associated with Antarctica? These large animals cannot live on land full-time like the tiny critters named above. Physical conditions in this frozen land are far too harsh for most of the year. Large animals come ashore just to bear young. Only the seas provide them enough food and shelter to live.

Hints

First describe what happens as the seasons change. Then describe how the animals respond to that change.

Use the Hints on this page to help you answer the questions.

1 The table contains sentences from the passages about Antarctica.

From "A Desert of Ice"	From "Antarctica's Life"
"The sun shines continuously from mid-September to mid-March, then disappears for the other half of the year."	"These year-round dwellers become inactive during the cold, dark winters, but they wake when daylight arrives and the air warms."

Use the information in the table to describe how animals that live in Antarctica year-round respond to the change of seasons there.

_____

_____

_____

_____

_____

The first passage describes Antarctica's climate—its yearly patterns of temperature, sunlight, and precipitation. The second passage describes how life survives on Antarctica. You can use facts about a place's climate to explain how animals survive there.

2 The table contains facts from the two passages about Antarctica.

From "A Desert of Ice"	From "Antarctica's Life"
• The average temperature in the warmest month is –28°C. • The sun shines over Antarctica for only half the year.	• Seals only come ashore to bear and raise young. • They return to the seas to find enough food to live.

Using all of the facts in the table as details, explain why seals cannot live on land in Antarctica the whole year round.

_____

_____

_____

_____

_____

Read the passages. Then answer the questions that follow.

A Short History of Easter Island

by Monique Jenkins

1   Easter Island is one of the most remote, inhabited islands in the world. It is in the Pacific Ocean about 3,780 kilometers east of South America. It was formed by three volcanoes which are now extinct. As far as inhabited islands go, Easter Island is quite small. It measures just 101 square kilometers, which is the size of San Francisco.

2   Scientists believe that the island was settled between 1,200 and 1,600 years ago by Polynesians. They called the island Rapa Nui. These first inhabitants, called the Rapanui, flourished. Scientists believe that as many as 7,000 people once lived on the tiny island. The earliest inhabitants moved tons of volcanic rock and used it to carve the enormous statues that look out over the island's landscape.

3   Rapa Nui remained isolated from other humans for hundreds of years. Then in 1722, a Dutch captain, Jacob Roggeveen, discovered it. His ship arrived on Easter Sunday, so he named the island "Easter Island." He estimated that 2,000 to 3,000 people lived there. Fifty years later, Captain James Cook came to Easter Island. He counted about 600 people living in misery. Clearly, something had gone terribly wrong. Beginning in 1864, Christian missionaries arrived on the island. They found a society whose members were constantly at war with each other. The population on Easter Island continued to decline.

4   Finally, the South American country Chile laid claim to Easter Island. In 1966, the island was made open to tourists. Finally, in 1995, it became a UNESCO World Heritage Site. This means that governments around the world help to protect the island so that future generations of people can visit and enjoy it. Today Easter Island has about 4,000 inhabitants. Some of them are descended from the Rapanui people.

Easter Island's Decline

by Erik Lehman

1　　More than 1,000 years ago, a civilization thrived on Easter Island. The island's rich soil yielded harvests of sweet potatoes, and the inhabitants (called the Rapanui) ate chickens they raised and kept. The Rapanui had a lot of spare time, and they used it to carve huge stone statues, called *moai*. The average moai was 4 meters tall. The larger ones measured more than 30 meters tall and weighed 80 tons. The island boasts 600 of these mysterious figures.

2　　Part of the mystery is how these people moved the statues around the island. Sixty years ago, a man named Thor Heyerdahl sought to explain it. He did an experiment and showed how people could have placed the statues on huge logs. Then they rolled heavy weights long distances atop the logs. He proved this process would have worked.

3　　Logs come from trees, but the Easter Island of today is almost completely treeless. Where did the trees go? Scientists concluded that the Rapanui cut down most of the trees and used them to move the statues. As the forests disappeared, so did the soil. Without trees on the island to prevent erosion, rainwater washed away the fertile earth, destroying the farmland. With fewer crops, people became hungry and fought over the food that was available. The island's population plummeted from a peak of 7,000 to just a few hundred.

4　　Today Easter Island is still treeless, but its population has grown. Now the people who live there welcome tourists who visit the grand statues and spend money. Ironically, the statues that indirectly led to Easter Island's fall are now helping to heal it.

Answer Form　**Number Correct** ╱ 1

1　Ⓐ　Ⓑ　Ⓒ　Ⓓ

1　Read these sentences from "A Short History of Easter Island."

> Fifty years later, Captain James Cook came to Easter Island. He counted about 600 people living in misery. Clearly, something had gone terribly wrong.

According to "Easter Island's Decline," what was one cause of this misery?

A Thor Heyerdahl ruined the farmland by showing how the statues were made.

B The soil was formed from volcanic rock, so it was not good for raising food crops.

C The Rapanui cut down all the trees, which eroded farmland for growing crops.

D The population fell from a peak of 7,000 people to just a few hundred.

2 The time line below shows some events described in "A Short History of Easter Island."

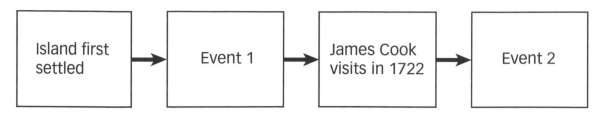

| Island first settled | → | Event 1 | → | James Cook visits in 1722 | → | Event 2 |

Find an event described in "Easter Island's Decline" that could go into the box that contains "Event 1." Describe that event on the line below.

_____

Now, find a different event described in "Easter Island's Decline" that could go into the box that contains "Event 2." Describe that event on the lines below.

_____

3 According to "A Short History of Easter Island," the island went through great changes between Jacob Roggeveen's visit in 1722 and the arrival of a group of missionaries in 1864. Describe one of these changes. Then explain a possible cause of that change. Use at least **one** detail from each passage in your answer.

_____

_____

_____

_____

_____

_____

 **✓ Self Check** *Go back and see what you can check off on the Self Check on page 211.*

Read the article. Then answer the questions that follow.

The Layers of Earth's Atmosphere

by Tawni Walker

1   Earth is surrounded by invisible gases that form a thin protective blanket that we call the atmosphere. It contains the oxygen we breathe. It also holds other important gases such as nitrogen, carbon dioxide, water vapor, and ozone.

2   Our atmosphere lets us breathe, but it is important for several other reasons. It burns and destroys meteors headed toward Earth's surface. It keeps our planet from having extreme temperature changes. Without this protective blanket, we would have hot days and freezing nights. One part of Earth's atmosphere, called the ozone layer, protects us from the Sun's harmful rays.

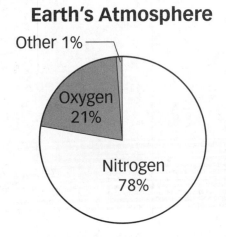

Earth's Atmosphere

3   The atmosphere is divided vertically into four layers based on temperature: the troposphere, the stratosphere, the mesosphere, and the thermosphere.

Prefix	Prefix Meaning
Tropo–	change
Strato–	layer
Meso–	middle
Thermo–	heat

Troposphere

4   The **troposphere** begins at Earth's surface and extends up to 12 miles (20 km) high. This is the layer of the atmosphere in which we live. Almost all weather occurs in this region.

5   If you were to walk from the bottom of a mountain to its top, you would notice the air getting thinner and the temperature dropping. This is the general pattern from the bottom to the top of the troposphere. At Earth's surface, the average temperature is around 62°F (17°C). At the top of the troposphere, the average temperature is around –60°F (–51°C).

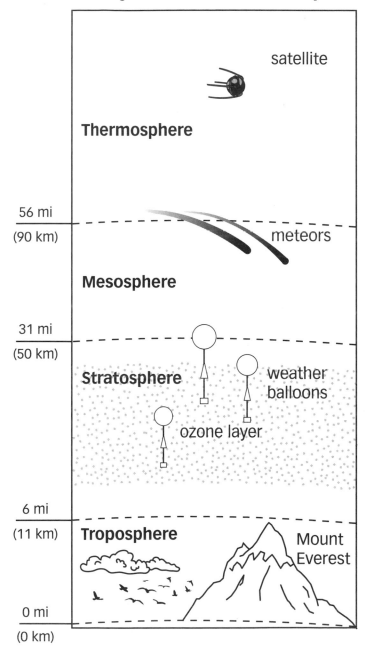

The Layers of Earth's Atmosphere

Stratosphere

6   The **stratosphere** starts at the top of the troposphere. It then rises to about 31 miles (50 km) above Earth's surface. From the bottom to the top, the temperature increases from an average of –60°F (–51°C) to 5°F (–15°C). The stratosphere holds 19 percent of the atmosphere's gases.

Mesosphere

7   The **mesosphere** begins at the top of the stratosphere. It climbs to about 56 miles (90 km) above Earth's surface. From bottom to the top, the temperature decreases from about 5°F (–15°C) to as low as –184°F (–120°C). The air keeps getting thinner and thinner. However, gases in the mesosphere are still thick enough to create friction when meteors enter the atmosphere, slowing them down as they hurtle toward Earth. This causes the meteors to burn up, leaving fiery trails in the night sky.

Thermosphere

8   Above the mesosphere is the **thermosphere**. This layer rises up to 375 miles (600 km) above Earth. The temperature shoots up, reaching as high as 3,600°F (2,000°C) near the top. The gases of the thermosphere are much thinner than those in the mesosphere.

9   The next time you look up at the sky, remember this: You are at the very bottom of the lowest layer of a vast ocean of gas that rises hundreds of miles above the clouds.

1 How does the circle graph help the reader understand the information in paragraph 1 of "The Layers of Earth's Atmosphere"?

A It shows that carbon dioxide, water vapor, and ozone make up less than 1% of Earth's atmosphere.

B It shows that more than 90% of Earth's atmosphere is made up of water vapor and oxygen.

C It shows that oxygen, nitrogen, and water vapor make up just 90% of Earth's atmosphere.

D It shows that gases like carbon dioxide, oxygen, and nitrogen are only a tiny fraction of Earth's atmosphere.

2 Read this sentence from paragraph 2 of "The Layers of Earth's Atmosphere."

Our atmosphere lets us breathe, but it is important for several other reasons.

How does the author support this point?

A by listing some of the gases that make up Earth's atmosphere

B by showing a diagram of the layers of Earth's atmosphere

C by telling about some other functions Earth's atmosphere serves

D by describing in detail the four layers of Earth's atmosphere

3 In "The Layers of Earth's Atmosphere," what information does the diagram provide to the reader that the text by itself does not?

A It describes how the atmosphere protects us from the Sun's dangerous rays.

B It identifies the location of the ozone layer within Earth's atmosphere.

C It shows how many miles and kilometers each layer is above Earth's surface.

D It presents the different types of weather that take place within the atmosphere.

Read the article. Then answer the questions that follow.

Air Works for Me

from *The Courage to Soar*, National Aeronautics and Space Administration

1   Did you know that we live at the bottom of an ocean? It is an ocean of air. We take the air around us for granted. We can't see it. We only feel it or notice it when the wind blows. So why pay any attention to it? We all know that air is necessary for life. Animals need the oxygen in air. Plants need the carbon dioxide in air.

2   Air is important to us in many other ways, too. It dries our clothes and vacuums our floors. It lifts kites and airplanes. We ride on it and can even sleep on it. As you explore all the ways air works for you, you may be surprised.

Air Is Pushy

3   Air is matter. It takes up space and it has mass. Because air has mass, Earth's gravity attracts it and gives it weight. And because it has weight, it presses on things—it exerts pressure. Think about it. You have mass. Your body is made up of millions of molecules. That means Earth's gravity gives you weight. Because you have weight, you exert pressure. Right now, you are probably sitting on a chair, a desk, or the floor. Therefore, you are exerting pressure on the chair, the desk, or the floor. Wherever you go, you exert pressure because you have weight.

4   The pressure, or push, caused by air is called air pressure. Air pressure is a very strong force. It can make a hot air balloon rise into the sky. It can crush a can. It can hold water in a glass that is upside down. Try the following experiment.

Is This Magic?

5   Fill a plastic cup half-full of water. Take some of the water and rub it along the rim of the cup to make a good seal. Lay an index card on top. Lay your hand on the index card and turn the cup upside down. Take your hand away. The air pressure will hold the water in the cup!

6   Since we are sitting at the bottom of an ocean of air, the air is always pressing on us. Air pressure changes as you go higher or lower in the atmosphere. As you travel higher in the sky, air pressure goes down. This is because the higher you go, the less air there is pressing down on you from above.

7   Picture yourself at the bottom of the ocean of air. All of the air above you is pushing on you. Now, picture yourself at the top of a very high mountain. There is less air above you. So there is less pressure on you.

4 The author of "Air Works For Me" uses the science experiment of the cup of water and the index card as evidence to support what point?

A Air pressure can be a much stronger force than most people realize.

B More water in the cup means more air pressure to push down on the card.

C Like air, your body has mass because it is made up of millions of molecules.

D Air is necessary for life because it carries the oxygen all animals need.

5 Answer Parts A and B below.

Part A

What point does the author of "Air Works for Me" make about air?

A It can be used in magic tricks.

B It has both mass and weight.

C We need not pay attention to it.

D It is important to us in many ways.

Part B

Which sentence from the article **best** supports the answer to Part A?

A "We only feel it or notice it when the wind blows."

B "We all know that air is necessary for life."

C "It dries our clothes and vacuums our floors."

D "The air pressure will hold the water in the cup!"

6 Look at the picture that goes with "Air Works For Me." How does the picture help the reader understand the concepts given in the passage?

A It helps the reader understand that it is impossible to remove the index card from the rim of the cup once you turn the cup upside down.

B It shows the reader how to make the water inside the cup turn into air pressure to keep the index card from falling off.

C It shows the reader that the cup should be entirely upside down before letting go of the index card, or the experiment may not work correctly.

D It helps the reader see how important it is to keep a hand underneath the cup to make the experiment work correctly.

7 Using details from **both** "The Layers of Earth's Atmosphere" and "Air Works for Me," answer the following questions:

• What is the troposphere?
• What are two qualities of the troposphere that living things need to survive?

Write your answer in paragraph form.

_____

_____

_____

_____

_____

_____

Performance Task—Extended Response

8 | The Earth's atmosphere is an invisible ocean of air. But not all of the parts of this ocean are the same. How are the upper layers of the atmosphere different than bottom layer? Use details from both passages to support your answer.

In your answer, be sure to
- tell what the bottom layer of the atmosphere is like
- tell how the upper layers of the atmosphere differ from the bottom layer
- use details from both passages to support your answer

Check your writing for correct spelling, grammar, capitalization, and punctuation.

_____

_____

_____

_____

_____

_____

_____

_____

_____

_____

_____

Have you ever had this experience? You start reading a story that begins something like this: "Long, long ago, when the earth was very new, the animals had no fire." You to think to yourself, "Oh no! I've read this before." But as you read on, you realize it's not the same story at all. The topic of the tale is the same—how fire and light were brought to earth—but the characters and events are different from the other story you read. This experience often happens to readers because literature has many topics and patterns that appear again and again. The more you read such stories, the more **knowledge** and **ideas** you gain from and about them. You can then **integrate** (put together) what you learn to understand the stories of people from around the world.

That's a surprise! This isn't the same story at all!

In this unit, you'll compare and contrast stories that have similar topics. You'll compare and contrast stories that have similar patterns of events. So, when you begin to read a story and you think, "Oh no! I've read this before," don't close that book. You might be in for a welcome surprise.

✓ Self Check

Before starting this unit, check off the skills you know below. As you complete each lesson, see how many more you can check off!

I know how to:	Before this unit	After this unit
compare and contrast the topics of stories, myths, and literature from various cultures.	☐	☐
compare and contrast the themes of stories, myths, and literature from various cultures.	☐	☐
compare and contrast patterns of events in stories, myths, and literature from various cultures.	☐	☐

CCSS

RL.4.7: Make connections between the text of a story or drama and a visual or oral presentation of the text, identifying where each version reflects specific descriptions and directions in the text.

What happens in your mind when you read a story? Do you picture the setting, see the characters, hear their voices, and imagine what's happening? If the descriptions of the setting, characters, and dialogue are strong, that's exactly what should happen. Your imagination plays an even bigger role when you read the script of a play. That's because a script contains mainly dialogue and stage directions. You need to read these features carefully to understand the setting, characters, and events.

Hearing stories read or seeing plays performed are different experiences than reading them. Other people (narrators, directors, and actors) have decided what the setting looks like and how the characters will act and sound. Those people may also have changed details and added features such as music and sound effects. It can be great fun to compare the text of stories and scripts with their spoken and staged performances.

Reread the script of the play about William Tell on page 64. In the table below, tell how you learned about the setting, the characters, and the events. Then listen to the recording of the same play and complete the second row of the table.

Medium	Setting	Characters	Events
Script			
Recording			

 In a small group, talk about the differences between the written and recorded versions of the play. Try to figure out the reason behind each difference.

Lesson 25 Part 1: Introduction 👥

Comparing Topics and Themes in Stories

CCSS

RL.4.9: Compare and contrast the treatment of similar themes and topics (e.g., opposition of good and evil) . . . in . . . traditional literature from different cultures.

Theme: *Wishes*

You've probably read stories about kids facing hard choices, good heroes fighting evil villains, or families looking for a better life. These are all examples of story **topics**. A story's topic can often be told with a sentence that begins, "This story is about . . . ."

Two stories can have the same topic but end up being different. For example, the two stories below have similar topics, but their differences are probably more important.

The Jealous Bluebird	The Sad Frog
Rabbit and Mouse had been friends forever. But Bluebird, who was jealous, tried to separate them. "I will grant you each one wish," said Bluebird. "I wish to travel to a faraway land," Rabbit said. Bluebird granted the wish, noting with a smirk that Rabbit did not wish he could also return. But Mouse was not fooled. "I wish that my friend will always find his way home." And Bluebird had no choice but to grant this wish, too.	Once there lived a frog who wished she could fly. She went to a heron and asked the heron to teach her. "Flying is easy," said the heron. "Just flap your wings like this." And the heron flew away before the frog could say, "But I have no wings." The frog hopped away sadly, wishing for wings she could never have. She didn't realize that a snake near a rock had heard everything and was wishing he could hop as gracefully as the frog.

"The Jealous Bluebird" and "The Sad Frog" share a topic. They are both about what can happen when talking animals (and people, too) make wishes. But in other ways the stories are different. For example, they have different themes. The **theme** of a story is a lesson told through the story's events and characters. Stories with similar topics can have different themes, as the table below shows.

Story	Topic	Theme
The Jealous Bluebird	What can happen when wishes are made.	True friends will find their way back to each other.
The Sad Frog	What can happen when wishes are made.	It is better to value your talents than to wish for someone else's.

To figure out a story's topic, ask yourself: "What is this story about?" To figure out a story's theme, ask yourself: "What is this story trying to teach me?" And when you compare topics and themes, a table like the one above can keep your ideas organized.

Read the folktale about a peasant who plans to steal cucumbers.

Genre: **Folktale**

The Peasant and the Cucumbers   *by Leo Tolstoy*

A peasant once went to the gardener's to steal cucumbers. He crept up to the cucumbers and thought, "I will carry off a bag of cucumbers, which I will sell; with the money I will buy a hen. The hen will lay eggs, hatch them, and raise a lot of chicks. I will feed the chicks and sell them; then I will buy me a young sow, and she will bear a lot of pigs. I will sell the pigs and buy me a mare; the mare will foal me some colts. I will raise the colts and sell them. I will buy me a house and start a garden. In the garden I will sow cucumbers and will not let them be stolen but will keep a sharp watch on them. I will hire watchmen and put them in the cucumber patch, while I myself will come on them, unawares, and shout, 'Oh, there, keep a sharp lookout!'" And this he shouted as loud as he could. The watchmen heard it, and they rushed out and beat the peasant.

Explore how to answer these questions: *"What are the topic and the theme of 'The Peasant and the Cucumbers'?"*

The topic of a story is what the story is about. The topic is often a one-sentence summary.

This story is about a _____

_____.

A theme is a lesson told through the main events and the characters. Read the table below.

What Are the Main Events?	What Does the Main Character Do?
• The peasant tries to steal cucumbers. • The peasant starts daydreaming about what will happen after he gets the cucumbers. • The peasant accidentally shouts and is caught.	• The peasant wants to become rich. • The peasant can't keep his mind on his task. • The peasant makes a mistake while daydreaming.

Based on details given in the table above, describe a likely theme of this story.

_____

_____

_____

Read this folktale about a man who receives a gift from a neighbor. Then read and answer the question that follows.

Genre: **Folktale**

The Flask of Oil   *an Indian folktale*

A poor man received from a kind and wealthy neighbor the gift of a large and valuable flask of oil. Delighted, the poor man carefully put it onto the top shelf in his home. One evening, as he was gazing at it, he said, "If I should sell it, I could buy five sheep. Every year I should have lambs. If I sold the lambs, I would be rich enough to marry and perhaps have a son. And what a fine boy he would be! But if he should disobey me"— and he raised the staff in his hand—"I should punish him thus!" So saying, he swung the staff, knocking the flask off the shelf so that the oil ran over him from head to foot.

Close Reading

The man daydreams about what he could do with the oil. How is this similar to what the peasant in "The Peasant and the Cucumbers" does? **Underline** one sentence in each story that seems similar to a sentence in the other story.

Hint

In what way are the men in the two stories the same?

Circle the correct answer.

How are "The Peasant and the Cucumbers" and "The Flask of Oil" similar?

A   Both are about wealthy neighbors who donate gifts.

B   They are both about men who steal valuable goods.

C   Both are about men who dream of having richer lives.

D   They are both about men who are punished for stealing.

✏️ Show Your Thinking

On the lines below, explain why you chose the answer you did. Refer to at least one detail from each story in your explanation.

_____

_____

_____

Read the two folktales. Use the Study Buddies and the Close Readings to guide your reading.

Genre: **Folktale**

Here are two stories. The stories are side-by-side, so I'm probably going to be asked to compare them. The titles tell me that both are folktales about princesses. I'll start by figuring out the topic and the theme of the first story.

Close Reading

After reading "Juvadi and the Princess," write down in the space below what you think the topic of the story is. Start with this sentence: "This story is about . . . ."

Juvadi and the Princess *a folktale from Italy*

1   One day, Juvadi the village fool walked by the castle and saw the princess standing at a window. Upon hearing her lovely laugh, Juvadi said, "May you fall in love with me!" And the princess immediately fell in love with him.

2   But the king was embarrassed. His daughter loved a fool! He asked his council, "How should I punish this shame?"

3   They answered, "Put them both into a cask and roll it over a cliff. You will never see them again." And so it was done.

4   As the cask rolled along, Juvadi cried, "Let me out! I'll give you figs and raisins." So saying, he threw handfuls of figs and raisins out of the cask. The cask stopped rolling at a level spot. Juvadi broke open the cask, and they got out.

5   A frog was nearby, and it laughed so hard that a wart on its neck disappeared. The frog was happy about this, so she said to Juvadi, "What is your wish? I can do everything, and will do something good for you."

6   Juvadi answered, "Make a house for me and the princess, for we wish to marry, but we have no place to live."

7   The frog said, "Here shall be a palace, with all the comforts of the world." Suddenly a beautiful palace was there, and Juvadi happily went inside with the princess.

8   The princess loved Juvadi, but she also knew him very well. "Now," she said. "I will marry you. But first we must find a wish that will drive out your stupidity."

Genre: **Folktale**

Hans and the Princess   *a German folktale*

After reading "Juvadi and the Princess," I've got some idea of its topic and theme. When I finish "Hans and the Princess," I'll compare the topics and themes. I can use a table like the one on page 247 to organize my ideas.

Close Reading

The characters and events in both stories are similar, but "Hans and the Princess" has a different ending. This means that "Hans" might have a theme that "Juvadi" does not. In the last two paragraphs of "Hans," **circle** at least two words or phrases that seem connected to a lesson the story is teaching you.

1   A king wished to know whom his daughter would marry. He sent his favorite dog to find her future husband. The dog dragged back Hans, the ugly and stupid village fool.

2   The embarrassed king put the princess and Hans in a casket and set them out to sea. The princess cried out, "You horrible fool. How is it that you are my future husband?"

3   "I wished for it," said Hans. "All my wishes come true."

4   "If that is so," she said, "then wish us something to eat." So Hans wished for a plate of potatoes, which she devoured.

5   Hans then said, "I wish for a grand ship." They appeared on a proud vessel, fully crewed and forging back to land.

6   Upon reaching shore, Hans declared, "Here there shall be a castle, and within it shall dwell the princess and her handsome, intelligent husband." Upon saying this, a castle appeared, and Hans became handsome and smart. The princess and Hans fell in love, married, and lived happily.

7   Years later, the princess' father was out riding and stumbled upon the castle. The king did not recognize his daughter, but she knew him. She treated him well, but before he left she hid a golden cup in his pocket. The princess then accused him of having stolen the cup.

8   The king protested that he did not know how the cup had come into his pocket. The princess said, "Do you see, now, how it feels to be treated unfairly?" She revealed herself as his daughter and forgave him. The king, overjoyed, named the princess and Hans as his heirs. Upon the king's death, Hans and the princess became king and queen.

Hints

Read each answer choice carefully. Only one answer choice names a topic common to both stories.

Use the Hints on this page to help you answer the questions.

1 How are "Juvadi and the Princess" and "Hans and the Princess" similar?

   A Both stories are about kings who are treated unfairly.

   B Both stories are about kings who lose their daughters forever.

   C Both stories are about wishes that go terribly wrong.

   D Both stories are about fools who marry princesses.

Some of the choices are themes you might have heard of, but you need to pick the theme of the stories you just read.

2 Which is a theme expressed by both of the folktales?

   A Putting your trust in a fool is a bad idea.

   B Love can overcome unexpected challenges.

   C Children should listen to the wisdom of their parents.

   D Hard work, not wishes, are what help people succeed.

At the end of "Hans and the Princess," what does the King learn? What details show that he has learned this lesson?

3 Because the stories end differently, "Hans and the Princess" has a theme that "Juvadi and the Princess" does not. Describe what you think this other theme in "Hans and the Princess" could be. Use one detail from "Hans and the Princess" to support your answer.

_____

_____

_____

_____

_____

_____

_____

_____

_____

Read the following folktales. Then answer the questions that follow.

The Two-Headed Weaver

a tale from The Panchatantra

1   In a certain place there lived a weaver by the name of Mantharaka, which means "the simpleton." One day, while weaving cloth, the wooden pieces on his loom broke. He took an ax and set forth to find some wood. He found a large sissoo tree at the ocean's shore, and said aloud, "Now this is a large tree. If I fell it, I will have wood enough for all my weaving tools."

2   Having thus thought it through, he raised his ax to begin cutting. However, a spirit lived in this tree, and he said, "Listen! This tree is my home. . . ."

3   The weaver said, "Then what am I to do? If I don't find a good tree, then my family will starve. You will have to go somewhere else. I am going to cut it down."

4   The spirit answered, "Listen, I am at your service. Ask whatever you would like, but spare this tree!"

5   The weaver said, "If that is what you want then I will go home and ask my friend and my wife, and when I return, you must give me what I ask for."

6   The spirit promised, and the weaver, beside himself with joy, returned home. Upon his arrival in his city he saw his friend, the barber, and said, "Friend, I have gained control over a spirit. Tell me what I should demand from him!"

7   The barber said, "My dear friend, if that is so then you should demand a kingdom. You could be king, and I would be your prime minister. . . ."

8   The weaver spoke, "Friend, so be it! But let us also ask my wife."

9   Having said this, he went quickly to his wife and said to her, "Dear one, today I have gained control over a spirit who will grant me one wish. Hence I have come to ask for your advice. Tell me, what should I ask for? My friend the barber thinks that I should request a kingdom."

10   She answered, "Oh, son of your excellence . . . . a king's life is an unending procession of annoyances. He must constantly worry about friendships, animosities, wars, servants, defense alliances, and duplicity. . . . Never envy the life of a king."

11   The weaver said, "You are right. But what should I ask for?"

12   She answered, "You can now work on only one piece of cloth at a time. That is barely enough to pay for the necessities. You should ask for another pair of arms and a second head so that you can work on two pieces of cloth at once, one in front of you, and one behind you. . . ."

13   After hearing this he spoke with joy, "Good, you faithful wife! You have spoken well, and I will do what you say. That is my decision."

14   With that he went to the spirit and let his will be known, "Listen, if you want to fulfill my wish, then give me another pair of arms and another head."

15   He had barely spoken before he was two-headed and four-armed. Rejoicing, he returned home, but the people there thought that he was a demon and beat him with sticks and stones, until he fell over dead. . . .

The Ridiculous Wishes

by Charles Perrault, Old Time Stories Told by Master Charles Perrault

1   There was once a poor woodcutter who, tired of his hard life . . . declared that in all his days heaven had not granted even one of his wishes. One day in the woods, as the woodcutter was complaining of his unhappy lot, Jupiter appeared before him, his thunderbolts in his hands. . . .

2   "Have no fear," said Jupiter. "I have heard your complaints and I have come to show you how unfairly you judge me. Now listen! I am king of all the world and I promise to grant your first three wishes, no matter what they may be. . . ."

3   With these words, Jupiter returned to his heavens and the happy woodcutter, taking up his bundle of sticks, hurried to his home. "This is an important matter," he said to himself. "I certainly must have my wife's advice."

4   "Hey, Fanchon," he shouted, as he entered his cottage. "Light us up a good fire. We are rich for the rest of our lives. All we have to do is to make three wishes!"

5   With this, he told his wife what had happened, whereupon she in her imagination began to form a thousand plans. "Blaise, my dear, let us not spoil anything by our impatience. We must think things over very carefully. Let us put off our first wish until tomorrow. Let us sleep on it."

6   "I think you are right," said he. . . . Relaxing, he leaned back in his chair before the fire. "To match such a fine blaze," he said, "I wish we had a measure of sausage. It would go very well indeed!"

7   Scarcely had he spoken these words when his wife, to her great astonishment, saw a long link of sausage moving over to them like a snake from the chimney corner. She cried out in alarm, but realizing at once that this was the result of the wish which her foolish husband had made, she began to . . . scold him angrily. "When you might," she said, "have a kingdom, with gold, pearls, rubies, diamonds, fine clothes; and all you wish for is a sausage!"

8   "Alas," her husband replied. "I was wrong, I made a very bad choice. I admit my mistake. Next time I will do better."

9   "Yes! Yes!" said his wife . . . "To make such a choice as you did, you must be a donkey."

10   At this the husband became very angry. . . . "A curse on this and all sausages. I wish that it was hanging from the end of your nose!"

11   The wish was heard at once . . . and the sausage fastened itself on her nose. Fanchon had once been pretty, and—to tell the truth—this ornament did not have a very pleasing effect. . . .

12   "With my remaining wish I could very well still make myself a king," he said to himself. "But we must think of the queen, too, and her unhappiness if she were to sit on the throne with her new yard-long nose. She must decide which she wants, to be a queen with that nose or a woodcutter's wife and an ordinary person."

13   Whereupon his wife agreed that they had no choice. She would never have the riches and diamonds and fine clothes she had dreamed of, but she would be herself again if the last wish would free her from the frightful sausage on her nose.

14   And so the woodcutter did not change his lot. He did not become a king. His purse was not filled with gold. He was only too glad to use his remaining wish in restoring his poor wife to her former state.

Answer Form

1 Ⓐ Ⓑ Ⓒ Ⓓ   **Number**
2 Ⓐ Ⓑ Ⓒ Ⓓ   **Correct**   /2

1   Which of the following describes an important difference between "The Two-Headed Weaver" and "The Ridiculous Wishes"?

   A   "The Two-Headed Weaver" says that friends and family are a good source of advice. "The Ridiculous Wishes" says that people should trust themselves before listening to others.

   B   "The Two-Headed Weaver" says that accepting who you are can make you happy. "The Ridiculous Wishes" says that it is important to keep changing and improving.

   C   "The Two-Headed Weaver" says that people who change their lives can face problems. "The Ridiculous Wishes" says that people who accept their lives can be happy.

   D   "The Two-Headed Weaver" says that beauty matters more than riches. "The Ridiculous Wishes" says that riches matter more than beauty.

2 "The Two-Headed Weaver" and "The Ridiculous Wishes" share a topic and a theme. Which **best** describes the topic and the theme that the stories share?

   A Shared topic: A husband accidentally wishes for some kind of food.
       Shared theme: If you work hard, you will be ready for luck when it comes.

   B Shared topic: A poor couple wishes to become rich and powerful.
       Shared theme: People need to be careful about what they wish for.

   C Shared topic: A husband and wife argue over how to use their wishes.
       Shared theme: Having riches does not always make people happy.

   D Shared topic: A person wishes for something that ends up being unhelpful.
       Shared theme: What people want is not always what is good for them.

3 Each story teaches a lesson about listening to advice. Write a paragraph telling whether these lessons are similar or different. Use at least **two** details from the text to support your answer.

_____

_____

_____

_____

_____

_____

_____

_____

 **Self Check** *Go back and see what you can check off on the Self Check on page 245.*

Comparing Patterns of Events in Stories

CCSS

RL.4.9: Compare and contrast the treatment of . . . patterns of events (e.g., the quest) in stories [and] myths . . . from different cultures.

Theme: Stories of the Sun and Moon

Some stories get told again and again. Do the events in these stories seem familiar?

- The parents of a girl prepare her for one type of life. The girl decides she wants a different life than the one her parents planned for her.

- An orphaned boy is raised by animals. He grows up thinking that he, too, is an animal. Later, the boy learns he is human and must go live with people.

- A group of people needs something. Only one person can help them. The person must go on a journey to reach a goal and help the group. This is a **quest**.

When two or more stories present similar events in a similar way, they share a **pattern of events**. But stories that share a pattern of events aren't the same in every way. The cartoons below tell stories that share a pattern of events but also have differences.

The diagram below tells the pattern of events in the left panel of the cartoon.

| Tall boy reaches to touch the Sun. | → | Tall boy brags he can do something no one else can. | → | Crowd becomes angry at tall boy. |

Use the diagram below to tell about the pattern of events in the right panel.

| Girl flies to get a piece of the Sun. | → | _____ | → | _____ |

Comparing the patterns of events in similar stories can help you enjoy and understand each story better. You also learn something about the places the stories come from.

Read the story about a woman who talks to the Sun.

Genre: **Folktale**

Tara and the Sun   *by Emma Roundtree*

For many years, the clan faced hardship. The rivers dried up, the herds moved away, and the air became colder. The people feared they would freeze to death, alone on a cold and ruined Earth.

Tara couldn't bear to see her people suffer. So she braved the dangers of the Mountain. After many days she reached the top and called forth the Sun.

"If my people die," she told the Sun angrily, "You'll have no one to shine on, no one will be left to care about you, and you'll fade away."

The Sun mulled this over. "Very well," he said. "Here is a small piece of me."

Tara brought the piece of the Sun to the clan. Slowly, the air warmed, the herds returned, and the rivers once again began to flow.

Explore how to answer these questions: *"Based on the events in the story, is 'Tara and the Sun' a quest? How do you know?"*

In a quest, a person sets off on a journey to achieve an important goal, often to help other people. To figure out if "Tara and the Sun" is a quest, compare that definition of "quest" with the most important events in the story. To do this, complete the diagram below.

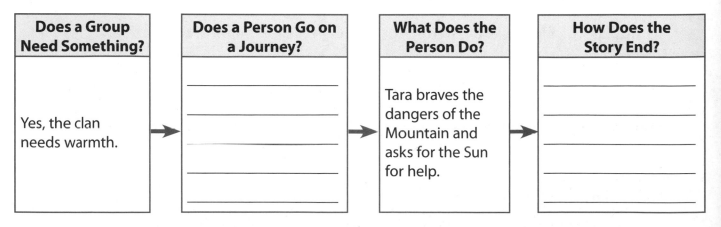

Does a Group Need Something?	Does a Person Go on a Journey?	What Does the Person Do?	How Does the Story End?
Yes, the clan needs warmth.		Tara braves the dangers of the Mountain and asks for the Sun for help.	

The events in the story are as follows: A group needs something. A person goes on a journey to help them. She reaches her goal and saves the clan. Therefore, "Tara and the Sun" is a quest.

Read the story about a boy who finds a piece of the Moon. Then read and answer the question that follows.

Close Reading

In the stories on pages 258 and 259, **circle** events that are similar in both stories. Then **underline** an event that is the opposite of an event in the other story.

Genre: **Folktale**

Lonely Moon   *by Luna Mer*

Long ago, a boy was walking through a field when he saw a glowing white stone. He picked it up. The moment his fingers touched the stone, Moon spoke through it to him. "I am lonely," said Moon. "I offer this part of myself to you. With it, we may speak." The boy and Moon became good friends.

As time passed, however, the Earth grew cold. Soon, all was frozen. Moon knew what had happened. The Moon-stone was harming the world. So, Moon lowered himself to Earth, took back the piece of himself, and returned to his lonely life in the sky.

Hint

Both the Sun and the Moon hand over pieces of themselves. But what happens after that?

Answer the question on the lines below.

Compare what happens when Tara gets a piece of the Sun with what happens when the boy gets a piece of the Moon. Use details from both stories in your comparison.

_____

_____

_____

_____

_____

_____

✎ **Show Your Thinking**

 Does "Lonely Moon" have the pattern of a quest? Discuss this question, using details from the story and what you know about quests.

Read the folktales. Use the Study Buddies and the Close Readings to guide your reading.

This lesson is about comparing and contrasting stories with similar patterns of events. When I read the stories, I'll look to see whether they tell similar events in a similar order.

Close Reading

Underline the sentences that explain how the monkeys try to get the moon.

Draw a box around a sentence that shows whether or not the monkeys were able to get the moon.

The Monkeys and the Moon

a Tibetan folktale, Tibetan Tales Derived from Indian Sources

1   In long-past times there lived a band of monkeys in a forest. As they rambled about they saw the reflection of the moon in a well, and the leader of the band said, "O friends, the moon has fallen into the well. The world is now without a moon. Ought not we to draw it out?"

2   The monkeys said, "Good; we will draw it out."

3   So they began to hold counsel as to how they were to draw it out. Some of them said, "Do not you know? The monkeys must form a chain, and so draw the moon out."

4   So they formed a chain, the first monkey hanging on to the branch of a tree, and the second to the first monkey's tail, and a third one in its turn to the tail of the second one. When in this way they were all hanging on to one another, the branch began to bend a good deal. The water became troubled, the reflection of the moon disappeared, the branch broke, and all the monkeys fell into the well and were disagreeably damaged.

5   A deity uttered this verse, "When the foolish have a foolish leader, they all go to ruin, like the monkeys which wanted to draw the moon up from the well."

Genre: **Folktale**

After reading the first story a few times, I know what events happened and in what order. Now I'll figure out the order of events in this story. To help me keep track of events in both stories, I can create diagrams like those on page 257.

Close Reading

Underline the sentences that explain how the king tries to get the sun and moon.

Draw boxes around any sentences that show whether or not the king was able to catch the sun and moon.

The King's Fire Dogs   *a Korean folktale*

retold by Mary Hoffman in Sun, Moon, and Stars

1   Heaven contains just as many countries as the Earth does. There is one called Land of Darkness where there is a king who keeps huge, fierce dogs called fire dogs. This king is always trying to think of ways to bring more light to his country.

2   One day, he called the biggest and most ferocious of his fire dogs and told it to go and bring him the sun. Off loped the dog and tried to seize the sun in his jaws. But the sun was so hot that it burned the dog's mouth. He snapped at it again and again but could not hold on. He had to go back to his master with his tail between his legs.

3   The king summoned his next biggest dog. He sent it to steal the moon for him, thinking that the moon wouldn't be as hot as the sun. But the second dog fared no better than the first. The moon was so cold that when he tried to bite it, the moon froze the dog's tongue to his mouth and made his teeth sing with pain. Hard as he tried, he could not hang on to the moon and had to spit it out. He too slunk back to the king.

4   Still, the king of darkness never gives up hope. Every now and then he sends one of his fire dogs to try and steal the sun or the moon. You can see the bite marks whenever there's an eclipse.

Hints

What goal do the characters in both stories share?

Use the Hints on this page to help you answer the questions.

1 How are the characters in "The Monkeys and the Moon" and "The King's Fire Dogs" similar?

- **A** They hope to bring more light to their part of the world.
- **B** They try to move the moon from one place to another.
- **C** They want to rescue the moon from a trap.
- **D** They succeed at bringing the moon to Earth.

In each story, how do the characters go about trying to accomplish their goals?

2 In what way do the stories differ from each other?

- **A** In "The Monkeys and the Moon," the monkeys try to get the moon themselves. In "The King's Fire Dogs," the king sends someone else to get the moon.
- **B** In "The Monkeys and the Moon," animals try to rescue the moon. In "The King's Fire Dogs," humans try to capture both the sun and the moon.
- **C** In "The Monkeys and the Moon," the monkeys damage the moon. In "The King's Fire Dogs," the dogs damage neither the sun nor the moon.
- **D** In "The Monkeys and the Moon," the moon is easily seen. In "The King's Fire Dogs," the moon stays hidden.

In the end, do the characters in these stories get what they wanted?

3 Describe one way in which the endings of the stories are similar. Use at least one detail from each story in your answer.

_____

_____

_____

_____

_____

_____

_____

_____

Read the two folktales. Then answer the questions that follow.

How Crow Brought Daylight

adapted from an Inuit folktale

1   Long ago when the world was young, the Inuit knew nothing about daylight. They lived and hunted under the stars of the northern darkness and thought nothing of it. Crow, however, had traveled far and wide and had seen daylight for himself. He told the Inuit about the light he saw at the horizon and how it made the earth glow with warmth and brilliance.

2   The people began to think how wonderful it would be to have light. They could hunt more efficiently and gaze upon each other's faces without the need of a fire. The village elders begged Crow to find the daylight and bring it to them.

3   Crow agreed to make the journey south, flying endless hours until he reached a village where the sky turned bright and filled with colors soft and wondrous. The village overflowed with trees and flowers and crops that grew strong and healthy. Crow saw a man who looked like the chief of the village and followed him home. Through an open window, Crow saw a ball glowing like a jewel resting in a corner. He knew the ball must be daylight. He waited until the man went outside again. Then he flew through the window, grabbed the ball, and flew away.

4   Crow's journey back north was long and even more tiring because he had to hold the ball in his beak. By the time he reached the Inuit, he was exhausted from his journey.

5   Crow looked like a spark of light as he entered the village. The people cheered as he grew closer, flapping his wings as hard as he could. But Crow could not hold the ball any longer. It fell to the ground and exploded into a brilliant light, chasing away the night. The sky became a bright blue. The shadowed mountains took on color and form.

6   As the people screamed in delight, Crow warned them that the daylight would not last forever. "I took only one ball of daylight from the people of the south," he explained. "It must rest every six months to regain its strength."

7   So, from that day until this, the Inuit have lived half a year in darkness and the other half in light. And they always treat Crow kindly, for it was he who first brought them daylight.

How Maui Snared the Sun

a Hawaiian folktale, Hawaiian Folk Tales: A Collection of Native Legends

1   Maui was the son of Hina-lau-ae and Hina, and they dwelt at a place called Makalia, above Kahakuloa, on West Maui. Now, his mother Hina made *kapas*. And as she spread them out to dry, the days were so short that she was put to great trouble and labor in hanging them out and taking them in day after day until they were dry.

2   Maui, seeing this, was filled with pity for her, for the days were so short that, no sooner had she got her *kapas* all spread out to dry, than the Sun went down, and she had to take them in again. So he determined to make the Sun go slower.

3   He first went to Wailohi, in Hamakua, on East Maui, to observe the motions of the Sun. There he saw that it rose toward Hana. He then went up on Haleakala, and saw that the Sun in its course came directly over that mountain.

4   He then went home again, and after a few days went to a place called Paeloko, at Waihee, he cut down all the cocoanut-trees, and gathered the fibre of the cocoanut husks in great quantity. This he manufactured into strong cord.

5   One Moemoe, seeing this, said tauntingly to him: "You will never catch the Sun. You are an idle nobody."

6   Maui answered: "When I conquer my enemy, and my desire is attained, I will be your death."

7   So he went up Haleakala again, taking his cord with him. And when the Sun arose above where he was stationed, he prepared a noose of the cord and, casting it, snared one of the Sun's larger beams and broke it off. And thus he snared and broke off, one after another, all the strong rays of the Sun.

8   Then shouted he exultingly: "You are my captive, and now I will kill you for going so swiftly."

9   And the Sun said: "Let me live, and you shall see me go more slowly hereafter. Behold, have you not broken off all my strong legs, and left me only the weak ones?"

10   So the agreement was made, and Maui permitted the Sun to pursue its course, and from that time on it went more slowly; and that is the reason why the days are longer at one season of the year than at another.

1 Which of the following correctly describes a similarity between "How Crow Brought Daylight" and "How Maui Snared the Sun"?

  A Both stories are about characters trying to predict the weather.

  B Both stories explain how the sun got its rays.

  C Both stories are about characters trying to get more daylight.

  D Both stories are about characters who have never seen daylight.

2 Which of the following correctly describes a difference between "How Crow Brought Daylight" and "How Maui Snared the Sun"?

  A Crow makes the daylight go away. Maui causes the Sun to stay.

  B Crow travels a long way. Maui does not have to travel.

  C Crow tries to help others. Maui tries to help only himself.

  D Crow carries a ball of daylight. Maui uses cord to slow the Sun.

3 Both "How Crow Brought Daylight" and "How Maui Snared the Sun" have the features of quests. Describe **two** features these stories have of quests. Use details from the text to support your descriptions.

First feature of a quest shared by both stories: _____

_____

_____

Second feature of a quest shared by both stories: _____

_____

_____

4 The diagram on the left side describes four events in "How Crow Brought Daylight." Fill out the diagram on the right side to describe four similar events in "How Maui Snared the Sun." Use details from the story in your answer.

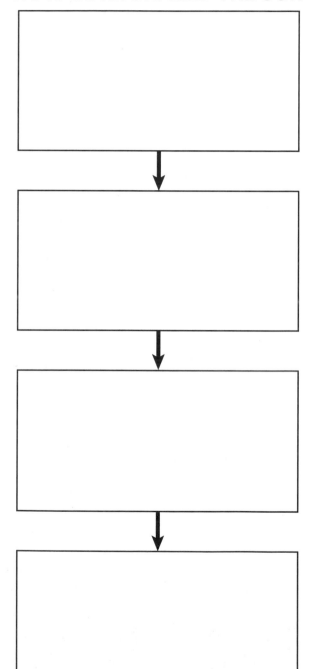

WHAT HAPPENS IN "HOW CROW BROUGHT DAYLIGHT"

The people live in darkness year-round. They beg Crow to find daylight so they can hunt and see each other's faces.

↓

Crow flies south, reaches a village, and finds a glowing ball of daylight in the hut of a chief.

↓

Crow steals the glowing ball and brings it back to the north. Upon reaching his people, he drops the ball.

↓

The ball explodes in light. The people now have six months of daylight each year. Crow's quest succeeds.

WHAT HAPPENS IN "HOW MAUI SNARED THE SUN"

✓ **Self Check** *Go back and see what you can check off on the Self Check on page 245.*

Read the following folktales. Then answer the questions that follow.

Ananse Brings Stories to the World

a folktale from West Africa

1   Ananse relaxed in his web one evening, watching the people sit by their fires. He saw that they were bored, and he wondered what he could do for them. Suddenly, he knew what they needed—stories! All people need stories to listen to and share.

2   Ananse realized that getting stories for the people would be a problem. Nyame, the sky spirit, kept all the stories locked in a wooden box. Ananse knew that this time his trickery wouldn't work. So he decided to approach the sky spirit and ask for the stories.

3   When the sun came up, Ananse spun a silk thread long enough to reach the sky. He scurried up the thread and approached Nyame. He bowed, and in his most polite voice he asked, "Nyame, great and generous spirit of the sky, the people are bored and restless. I want to share your stories with them. What is your price?"

4   Nyame burst out laughing and replied, "My price is high. To buy these stories, you must bring me Onini, the python, Osebo, the leopard, and Mmoboro, the stinging hornet. Capture these creatures and the stories will be yours."

5   Ananse slid down the silken thread, thinking, "What have I gotten myself into? Will I lose my life?" He used all his creativity to concoct a three-step plan.

6   The next day, Ananse charged into the forest carrying a palm branch. He shouted, "Onini, where are you? People say that you are shorter than this branch. Let's show them that they are wrong!"

7   The snake knew he was longer than the branch, so he willingly lay down on ground next to it. Ananse used his thread to tie the snake tightly to the branch and then offered him up to the sky spirit.

8   Next, Ananse went into the forest to find Osebo's route to the water hole. Along the path he stopped, dug a deep hole, and carefully covered it with sticks, dried leaves, and ashes from an old fire. He went home to eat, sleep, and hope for the best. In the morning, he went to the hole and found that Osebo was stuck in it. The leopard begged Ananse to help him, promising not to eat him.

9   Ananse pretended to help. He used a willow branch and more silk thread to pull the leopard out by his tail. Then he bound the leopard up with thread and offered him up to the sky spirit.

10   Now it was time to capture Mmoboro. Ananse carved out a calabash and filled it with water. He took the gourd and a large leaf and went to find Mmoboro's nest. Then he poured water over his head and over the nest. Just as the hornet swarmed out of the nest, Ananse cried, "The rains have come early. Come, take shelter in my calabash until the storm ceases."

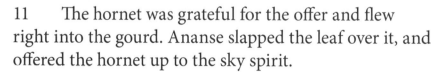

11   The hornet was grateful for the offer and flew right into the gourd. Ananse slapped the leaf over it, and offered the hornet up to the sky spirit.

12   The sky spirit accepted the final offering and called out, "Ananse has paid the price I asked for the stories. From now on they shall be known as 'spider stories.'" And he gave the beautiful wooden box of stories to Ananse, as he had promised.

Oodgeroo

a folktale from Australia

1   In the New Dreamtime, there lived an Aborigine woman. She had lost her tribe and longed to know the old stories that had belonged to her people. But she could only remember the stories of the New Dreamtime. Remembering the stories would be a problem because Old Dreamtime had stolen the stories and had hidden them away.

2   The woman decided to search for the old stories so her tribe would not be lost to her. She set off, carrying only an old sugar bag in case she needed to collect things.

3   Soon she came upon the ashes of a fire that her tribe had kindled long ago. She ran her fingers through the ashes and called upon Biami the Good Spirit to help her find her old tribe and its stories.

4   Biami answered her call. He told her to first find some paperbark trees and ask their permission to take some bark. Finding the trees was not difficult. The trees readily offered their bark to her, as they somehow knew that the woman was not greedy and would not take more than she needed. She stuffed some bark in her bag and traveled on.

5   She had not gone far when Biami came to her with a second instruction. The Good Spirit told her to return to the dead fire and collect the charred sticks that lay in the ashes. The woman placed the sticks in her bag with the bark. Biami appeared again and instructed the old woman to do this every time she wandered upon the dead fire of any lost tribe, not just her own.

6   The old woman traveled many miles. She thought she was alone, but she wasn't. Old Dreamtime didn't understand what the woman was doing, so he followed her everywhere she went. Each time she came upon the fire of a lost tribe, the old woman would gather the sticks and place them in her bag. When her bag was stuffed, she went to the secret-dreaming place of the old tribes. There, she called on Biami again, this time asking the Good Spirit to help her remember the old stories so she could find her tribe.

7   Biami loved her, so he opened her mind so that she could discover the old stories and her tribe. The woman took the charred sticks and bark from her bag and placed them on the ground. She scraped the sticks across the bark and saw that they made marks.

8   She sat there for many years, sketching the stories of long-lost tribes. She sat there until she had used up all the sticks and bark.

9   The paperbark trees had watched the woman over the years, so when they grew and blossomed the next season, they took the woman into their tribe as one of their own. They did this so she would never be without bark for her stories. They named her Oodgeroo. Oodgeroo had found the stories that were once hidden. Thankfully, Old Dreamtime had lost his power over her.

1   Use the following diagram to answer the question.

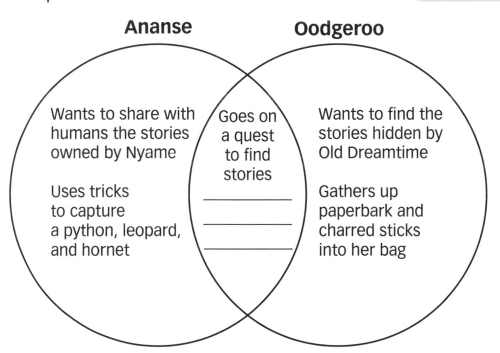

Which of these belongs on the blank lines in the diagram?

A   Follows instructions given by a spirit

B   Steals stories from powerful creatures

C   Writes down stories for people to have

D   Is welcomed by people into a tribe

2 Answer Parts A, B, and C below.

Part A

What do "Ananse Brings Stories to the World" and "Oodgeroo" have in common?

A characters who must search for stories

B animals that speak and behave like people

C heroes who succeed through tricking others

D spirits that demand payment for their help

Part B

Find a sentence in "Ananse Brings Stories to the World" with details that support the answer to Part A. Write that sentence on the lines below.

_____

_____

_____

Part C

Find a sentence in "Oodgeroo" with details that support the answer to Part A. Write that sentence on the lines below.

_____

_____

_____

3 Which statements is true about only **one** of the tales, **not** both of them?

   A Much of the action in the tale takes place in the forest.

   B A character follows several steps to find hidden stories.

   C A character in search of stories asks a spirit for help.

   D The spirit who has the stories offers a way to get the stories.

4 Stories are important to Ananse and Oodgeroo, but for different reasons. Ananse and Oodgeroo also have different plans for how to get the stories they want. Why does each character want stories? How are their plans for getting the stories different? Answer these questions, using details from the story.

Why Ananse wants stories: _____

_____

How Ananse plans to get the stories: _____

_____

_____

Why Oodgeroo wants stories: _____

_____

How Oodgeroo plans to get the stories: _____

_____

_____

_____

Performance Task—Extended Response

5 Both Ananse and Oodgeroo must face challenges in order to find the stories they seek. How are these challenges alike? How are they different?

In your answer, be sure to
- describe the challenges Ananse and Oodgeroo face in search of stories
- explain how each character's challenges are alike and different
- use details from both stories in your answer

Check your writing for correct spelling, grammar, capitalization, and punctuation.

_____

_____

_____

_____

_____

_____

_____

_____

_____

_____

_____

Ready® Common Core Language Handbook
Table of Contents

Conventions of Standard English		CCSS

Knowledge of Language

Vocabulary Acquisition and Use

Vocabulary Acquisition and Use *(continued)*

Lesson 1
Relative Pronouns and Adverbs

CCSS

L.4.1a: Use relative pronouns (*who, whose, whom, which, that*) and relative adverbs (*where, when, why*).

Introduction A **clause** is a group of words with a subject and a predicate. Some sentences include a **dependent clause**, which depends on, or gives more information about, the main clause. A dependent clause cannot stand alone as a sentence.

main clause	dependent clause
[Some restaurants offer meals]	[that come from different countries.]

- The **pronouns** *who, whose, whom, which,* and *that* can introduce a dependent clause. Use *who, whose,* and *whom* when talking about people. Use *that* and *which* when talking about things or places.

Many immigrants have a recipe **that** they brought from another country.

The recipe might have come from relatives **who** lived long ago.

- The **adverbs** *where, when,* and *why* can also introduce a dependent clause.

When Gina's parents lived in Italy, they owned restaurants.

Guided Practice Underline the dependent clause in each sentence. Circle the pronoun or adverb that introduces the clause.

Hint

A dependent clause can come at the beginning, middle, or end of a sentence.

1. Chinese restaurants are popular in San Francisco, where many Chinese Americans live.

2. People who live in the Northeast can enjoy wonderful Italian restaurants.

3. Tex-Mex, which became popular in the 1950s, is a blend of Mexican and American food.

4. Now I understand why there are so many Tex-Mex restaurants in the Southwest.

5. When I go out to eat, I love to try new foods.

6. My friend Kanti, whose family is from India, took me to a great Indian restaurant.

For numbers 1 and 2, which word in each sentence introduces a dependent clause?

1 San Francisco is one place where you will find Chinese hot pot dishes.

A one

B you

C where

D find

For numbers 3 and 4, which group of words in each sentence is a dependent clause?

3 I have a good friend whose family comes from China.

A a good friend whose

B I have a good friend

C family comes from China

D whose family comes from China

2 Chicken, pork, and fish are just some of the ingredients that might go into the hot pot.

A that

B are

C might

D just

4 When I eat at his house, his mother serves hot pot dishes.

A his mother serves hot pot dishes

B serves hot pot dishes

C When I eat at his house, his mother

D When I eat at his house

Lesson 2
Progressive Verb Tenses

CCSS
L.4.1b: Form and use the progressive (e.g., *I was walking; I am walking; I will be walking*) verb tenses.

Introduction The tense of a verb helps tell when something is happening. The **progressive tenses** show action that continues, or is ongoing. They combine a form of the helping verb *be* with a main verb that ends in *-ing*.

> helping verb   main verb
> She [is] [walking] in the woods today.

- **Present Progressive Tense:** To show continuing action in the present, use the present tense of *be*. Use *am* with the pronoun *I*. Use *is* with *he, she, it,* and singular nouns. Use *are* with *we, you, they,* and plural nouns.

  > I **am walking** with a friend. The sun **is shining**. We **are strolling**.

- **Past Progressive Tense:** To show continuing action in the past, use the past tense of *be*. Use *was* with *I, he, she, it,* and singular nouns. Use *were* with *we, you, they,* and plural nouns.

  > She **was walking** here yesterday. The birds **were chirping**.

- **Future Progressive Tense:** To show continuing action in the future, use the future tense of *be*.

  > I **will be coming** back tomorrow.

Guided Practice **Write the correct form of the verb in parentheses ( ) to show continuing action in each sentence.**

Hint

Look for time words and phrases, such as *yesterday*, *now*, and *next week*, to know when the action takes place.

1 Our scout troop _____ on a hike next week. (go)

2 I _____ last night to get ready for the trip. (pack)

3 Right now, I _____ about the weather forecast. (wonder)

4 At the moment, it _____ and very cold! (rain)

For numbers 1–5, which words should replace the underlined part of the sentence to make it correct?

1 Yesterday, we <u>will be hiking</u> to the top of a mountain.

    A was hiking

    B are hiking

    C were hiking

    D is hiking

2 At first, I <u>are struggling</u> with my heavy backpack.

    A is struggling

    B was struggling

    C were struggling

    D will be struggling

3 When we reached the top, my back <u>am aching</u>.

    A were aching

    B will be aching

    C are aching

    D was aching

4 Right now, I <u>is feeling</u> sore but proud.

    A are feeling

    B were feeling

    C am feeling

    D will be feeling

5 Tomorrow, my troop <u>were taking</u> an even longer hike.

    A will be taking

    B am taking

    C was taking

    D are taking

Lesson 3
Modal Auxiliaries

CCSS
L.4.1c: Use modal auxiliaries (e.g., *can*, *may*, *must*) to convey various conditions.

Introduction You know that a **helping verb** works with a main verb, or the verb that names a specific action or state of being. The helping verb and main verb create a *verb phrase*. Helping verbs can also be called **auxiliary verbs**. One special group of helping verbs include the following: *can, could, will, would, might, may, must,* and *should*.

| helping verb | main verb | | helping verb | main verb |

You [**should**] [exercise] regularly. Sports [**can**] [improve] your health.

• These special helping verbs show different conditions, or meanings.

Helping Verb	Meaning	Example
can	"able to"	I can play softball today.
could	"able to", "possibly"	I could play later.
will	"definitely, in the future"	I will play softball later.
would	"under a certain condition"	I would be on your team.
might	"possibly, now or in the future"	I might play Monday.
may	"possibly" or "allowed to"	You may play if you wish.
must	"definitely need to"	We must practice hard.
should	"expect to" or "need to"	We should win the game.

Guided Practice Circle the helping verb in each sentence. Underline the main verb that goes with the helping verb.

Hint

The word *not* is an adverb. It is *not* a helping verb. But it can come between a helping verb and a main verb to make the sentence negative.

1 People must play softball according to certain rules.

2 A team should have nine players on the field.

3 In slow-pitch softball, there might be one more player.

4 Teams may play from three to seven innings.

5 A tied score can push the game into extra innings.

6 With the creation of softball, people could play year-round.

7 Baseball players would enjoy softball in the off-season.

8 In summer 2016, softball will not be an Olympic sport.

Read the paragraph. The writer would like to replace the underlined phrases. Which verb phrase best replaces the underlined portion of each sentence in numbers 1–4?

People <u>are able to enjoy</u> softball all year round. Most players <u>are usually</u> between the ages of eight and seventy. Many schools have softball teams, but so do many businesses. Companies <u>often have</u> softball teams. Businesses play against other teams for fun or to raise money for charities. Most people <u>definitely agree</u> that the game is great fun.

---

1 People <u>are able to enjoy</u> softball all year round.

   A must enjoy

   B should enjoy

   C will enjoy

   D can enjoy

2 Most players <u>are usually</u> between the ages of eight and seventy.

   A will not be

   B must be

   C may be

   D would be

3 Companies <u>often have</u> softball teams.

   A must have

   B should not have

   C could have

   D may not have

4 Most people <u>definitely agree</u> that the game is great fun.

   A will agree

   B could agree

   C must agree

   D should not agree

Lesson 4
Order of Adjectives

CCSS
L.4.1d: Order adjectives within sentences according to conventional patterns (e.g., *a small red bag* rather than *a red small bag*).

Introduction An **adjective** is a word that describes a noun or a pronoun. Some adjectives describe by telling what kind or how many.

- Sometimes more than one adjective describes a noun or a pronoun.

> We saw **three interesting wooden** <u>statues</u> at the museum.

- Notice how the adjective *three* comes before *interesting* and *wooden*. When you use more than one adjective, it is important to place them in a certain order. Put the different kinds of adjectives in the order shown in this chart, going from left to right.

Number	Opinion	Size	Shape	Color	Material
three	pretty	huge	oval	green	leather
several	cute	tall	round	yellow	plastic

- Look at this example.

> two huge square
> There are ~~square two huge~~ murals near the exit.

Guided Practice **Read each sentence. Then write the underlined adjectives in the correct order.**

Hint

When you use more than one adjective before a noun, say the sentence aloud. If it doesn't sound right, look at the chart to see if you've put the adjectives in the correct order.

1 The museum has <u>metal beautiful blue</u> vases on display.

_____

2 <u>Round one crystal</u> vase comes from India.

_____

3 I see <u>tiny wonderful many</u> paintings on that wall.

_____

4 That painting includes <u>brick several tall</u> buildings.

_____

For numbers 1–5, choose the answer that has the underlined adjectives in the correct order.

1

A This artist created <u>square small green</u> paintings.

B This artist created <u>green square small</u> paintings.

C This artist created <u>square green small</u> paintings.

D This artist created <u>small square green</u> paintings.

2

A She also drew <u>graceful some gray</u> birds.

B She also drew <u>graceful gray some</u> birds.

C She also drew <u>some gray graceful</u> birds.

D She also drew <u>some graceful gray</u> birds.

3

A That watercolor has <u>beautiful blue wavy</u> lines.

B That watercolor has <u>wavy beautiful blue</u> lines.

C That watercolor has <u>beautiful wavy blue</u> lines.

D That watercolor has <u>wavy blue beautiful</u> lines.

4

A I love the <u>two silver small</u> teapots in this picture.

B I love the <u>silver two small</u> teapots in this picture.

C I love the <u>two small silver</u> teapots in this picture.

D I love the <u>small two silver</u> teapots in this picture.

5

A Did you notice the <u>red long silk</u> tablecloth?

B Did you notice the <u>long red silk</u> tablecloth?

C Did you notice the <u>silk red long</u> tablecloth?

D Did you notice the <u>red silk long</u> tablecloth?

👥 **Introduction** A **preposition** is a word that shows the relationship between other words in a sentence. Words such as *about, after, at, behind, by, during, for, in, on,* and *under* are prepositions.

- A **prepositional phrase** includes a preposition, a noun or pronoun that is the object of the preposition, and any words in between.

preposition   object of preposition

Myka looked [**at**] the large [tree].

- A prepositional phrase can describe a noun or a verb. It sometimes describes by telling *how, when, where,* or *what kind.*

Examples	What They Tell
Myka and Lily *went* outside **after** lunch.	*when* they went
They *sat* **under** the oak tree.	*where* they sat
It was a good *spot* **for** a tree house.	*what kind* of spot
Lily showed Myka a *book* **about** tree houses.	*what kind* of book
They *could build* a tree house **by** themselves.	*how* they could build

👥 **Guided Practice** Underline each prepositional phrase, and circle the preposition. Then finish the last two sentences by adding a prepositional phrase to each.

Hint

A prepositional phrase can come at the beginning, in the middle, or at the end of a sentence.

1 The tall oak tree was behind the house.

2 Myka and Lily would build their tree house in its branches.

3 During dinner, they discussed different ideas.

4 "Should we draw our plans after school?" Myka asked.

5 Their dad could buy wood and nails _____.

6 Myka and Lily decided to start building _____

_____.

For numbers 1–3, identify the prepositional phrase in each sentence.

1 The girls used solid wood planks for the tree house floor.

   A used solid wood

   B planks for

   C The girls used

   D for the tree house floor

For numbers 4 and 5, what does the underlined prepositional phrase tell?

2 Lily made a small window in one wall.

   A one wall

   B Lily made

   C in one wall

   D a small window

4 Myka and Lily hung a "Members Only" sign <u>on the door</u>.

   A when they hung the sign

   B where they hung the sign

   C what kind of sign they hung

   D how they hung the sign

3 Myka put curtains over the window.

   A over the window

   B put curtains

   C Myka put

   D the window

5 Then the girls had a discussion <u>about safety rules</u>.

   A what kind of discussion

   B when the discussion took place

   C where the discussion took place

   D how the discussion started

Lesson 6
Complete Sentences and Fragments

CCSS
L.4.1f: Produce complete sentences, recognizing and correcting inappropriate fragments. . . .

 Introduction A **sentence** is a group of words that tells a complete thought.

- A **complete sentence** has a subject and a predicate. The **subject** tells whom or what the sentence is about. The **predicate** tells what the subject does or is.

> subject   predicate
> [Nick and his friends] [listen to jazz music.]

- A **sentence fragment** is a group of words that is written as a sentence, but it does not tell a complete thought. It does not have a subject and a predicate. When you write, be sure your sentences are complete!

Sentence Fragments	Complete Sentences
Played the trumpet.	Two friends played the trumpet.
My brother and sister.	My brother and sister are in a band.

Guided Practice Read each group of words. Write *S* if it is a sentence or *F* if it is a fragment. Then write each fragment correctly as a complete sentence.

Hint

The subject of a sentence will always have a noun or pronoun. The predicate will always have a verb.

1 Jazz all over the world. _____

_____

2 In the early 1900s, jazz became popular. _____

_____

3 Was very different from other music at the time. _____

_____

4 Big bands played a kind of jazz called swing. _____

_____

5 Dancing to swing. _____

_____

For numbers 1 and 2, which group of words is a complete sentence?

1
- **A** Louis Armstrong influenced other musicians.
- **B** Louis Armstrong, one of the greatest jazz musicians.
- **C** Was one of the greatest jazz musicians of all time.
- **D** Was a huge influence on jazz music in general.

2
- **A** His music also exciting for dancing.
- **B** Because his music was so happy and lively.
- **C** Danced and listened to his upbeat music.
- **D** People loved to dance to his music.

For numbers 3 and 4, which choice changes the fragment into a complete sentence?

3 Developed a new way of playing.
- **A** Developed a new way of playing jazz music.
- **B** Developed a new way of playing his trumpet.
- **C** In the 1920s, developed a new way of playing.
- **D** Louis Armstrong developed a new way of playing.

4 Armstrong's jazz style.
- **A** Becoming famous, Armstrong's jazz style.
- **B** Armstrong's jazz style became famous.
- **C** Famous over the years, Armstrong's jazz style.
- **D** Armstrong's jazz style famous for years.

Lesson 7
Run-on Sentences

CCSS

L.4.1f: Produce complete sentences, recognizing and correcting inappropriate . . . run-ons.

Introduction You know that a **sentence** is a group of words that tells a complete thought. A **run-on sentence** is two or more sentences that run together with a comma between them or with no punctuation at all.

> **Run-on:** Julia is always helping other people she hardly has time for herself.
>
> **Run-on:** She tutors kids after school, she volunteers at a food pantry on weekends.

- One way to fix a run-on sentence is to split it into two sentences.

> **Correct:** Julia is always helping other people. She hardly has time for herself.

- Another way to fix a run-on sentence is to use a conjunction, such as *and*, *but*, *so*, *because*, or *while*, to join the two thoughts.

> **Correct:** She tutors kids after school, and she volunteers at a food pantry on weekends.

Guided Practice Read each sentence. Write *R* for run-on sentence or *C* for correct. Fix the run-on sentences by adding a conjunction or by dividing the thoughts into two sentences.

Hint

When you use the conjunction *and, or, so,* or *but* to combine two sentences, put a comma before the conjunction. Do not use a comma before the conjunction *because*.

1 My friends and I want to have a party for Julia's birthday. _____

_____

2 We hope to keep it a surprise, we will have to be careful. _____

_____

_____

3 The party will be at Stella's house her parents will help. _____

_____

_____

4 Stella will invite Julia over for a nice lunch that day. _____

_____

_____

For numbers 1 and 2, which choice is a run-on sentence?

1

A My friends and I admire Julia, but we worry about how busy she is.

B She doesn't have time for sports or movies.

C Donica and I decided that we could help Julia, we could take turns tutoring after school.

D I could tutor on Tuesdays, and Donica could tutor on Thursdays.

2

A Julia could still tutor on Mondays, there is no tutoring on Fridays.

B Julia needs a break, so she can have more time to see friends.

C Donica and I will talk to Julia and ask for her opinion.

D We know that she enjoys her volunteer work, and we don't want her to stop doing it.

For numbers 3 and 4, what is the best way to fix each run-on sentence?

3 Julia agreed to our plan she was happy to have the help.

A Julia agreed to our plan, she, was happy to have the help.

B Julia agreed to our plan. She was happy to have the help.

C Julia agreed to our plan, she was happy to have the help.

D Julia agreed to our plan, She was happy to have the help.

4 I enjoyed tutoring I decided to sign up for more days.

A I enjoyed tutoring, I decided to sign up for more days.

B I enjoyed tutoring but, I decided to sign up for more days.

C I enjoyed tutoring, so I decided to sign up for more days.

D I enjoyed tutoring and, I decided to sign up for more days.

Commonly Confused Words

CCSS
L.4.1g: Correctly use frequently confused words (e.g., *to, too, two; there, their*).

Introduction **Homophones** are words that sound alike but have different meanings and spellings. Homophones are easy to confuse because they sound the same!

- Watch out for the homophones *two*, *too*, and *to* in your writing. The homophones *there*, *their*, and *they're* are also easy to confuse.

Word	Meaning	Example
two	"a number"	Kira is excited about two things.
too	"also"	She loves swimming, but she loves writing, too.
to	"in a certain direction"	She goes to the pool almost every day.
there	"in that place"	The swim team practices there.
their	"belonging to them"	They try to improve their speed.
they're	"contraction for *they are*"	Next week they're having a big meet.

- Learn the spellings and meanings of these homophones, too!

no	"opposite of *yes*"
know	"to be aware of"

right	"correct" or "opposite of *left*"
write	"to put down on paper"

it's	"contraction for *it is*"
its	"belonging to *it*"

would	"under a certain condition"
wood	"part of a tree"

hours	"units of time"
ours	"belonging to *us*"

new	"opposite of *old*"
knew	"past tense of *know*"

Guided Practice **Circle the correct homophone in parentheses ( ).**

Hint

If you're not sure which spelling to use for a homophone, check the different spellings and their meanings in a dictionary.

1. Not many people (know, no) how fast Kira is.

2. They (wood, would) not want to compete against her if they did!

3. She has a (knew, new) coach who is helping her train.

4. He thinks (it's, its) possible for her to be on the Olympic team.

5. Kira is working hard to prove him (write, right).

6. (Their, There, They're) goal is for Kira to beat her own time.

For numbers 1–5, in which sentences are the underlined homophones spelled correctly?

1 **A** Kira spends at least <u>two hours</u> at the pool every day.

B Kira spends at least <u>too hours</u> at the pool every day.

C Kira spends at least <u>to ours</u> at the pool every day.

D Kira spends at least <u>two ours</u> at the pool every day.

2 **A** Her teammates practice with <u>their</u> team, <u>to</u>.

B Her teammates practice with <u>their</u> team, <u>too</u>.

C Her teammates practice with <u>there</u> team, <u>too</u>.

D Her teammates practice with <u>they're</u> team, <u>two</u>.

3 **A** <u>Its</u> not easy to be <u>there</u> each day after school.

B <u>Its</u> not easy to be <u>their</u> each day after school.

C <u>It's</u> not easy to be <u>they're</u> each day after school.

D <u>It's</u> not easy to be <u>there</u> each day after school.

4 **A** Kira <u>new</u> she <u>would</u> have less time for writing.

B Kira <u>knew</u> she <u>would</u> have less time for writing.

C Kira <u>knew</u> she <u>wood</u> have less time for writing.

D Kira <u>new</u> she <u>wood</u> have less time for writing.

5 **A** "I <u>know</u> I will <u>right</u> about my swimming someday," she says.

B "I <u>no</u> I will <u>write</u> about my swimming someday," she says.

C "I <u>know</u> I will <u>write</u> about my swimming someday," she says.

D "I <u>no</u> I will <u>right</u> about my swimming someday," she says.

Capitalizing Names of People

CCSS
L.4.2a: Use correct capitalization.

Introduction A noun that names *any* person, place, or thing is a **common noun**. A noun that names a *particular* person, place, or thing is a **proper noun**. When you write, capitalize proper nouns.

- The names of people are proper nouns.
- Some names include a title or initials. Capitalize them also.

People	
Mr. Gomez	Ms. Eileen M. Bryant
President Lincoln	Dr. Kuri Suzuki
P. F. Ling	Martin Luther King, Jr.

- Family titles such as *mom*, *dad*, *grandma*, *grandpa*, *aunt*, and *uncle* are capitalized only when they are used as a person's name. When they are used as common nouns, do not capitalize them.

I like visiting my **aunt**. Her name is **Aunt Shana**.

Guided Practice Write each sentence correctly. Add capital letters where they are needed.

Hint

Some titles used with names are abbreviations. They end with a period. For example, the title *Mr.* is an abbreviation for *Mister*, and *Jr.* is an abbreviation for *Junior*.

1 Our uncle, dr. castillo, told us about a civil rights leader.

_____

_____

2 Rev. dr. martin luther king, jr., was born on January 15, 1929.

_____

_____

3 His parents were rev. michael king, sr., and alberta williams king.

_____

_____

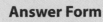
For numbers 1–4, in which sentence are capital letters used correctly?

1 **A** King studied about the famous civil rights leader, mahatma gandhi.

B King studied about the famous civil rights leader, Mahatma gandhi.

C King studied about the famous civil rights leader, mahatma Gandhi.

D King studied about the famous civil rights leader, Mahatma Gandhi.

2 **A** King's Father asked his son to become a pastor with him in Atlanta.

B King's father asked his son to become a Pastor with him in Atlanta.

C King's father asked his son to become a pastor with him in Atlanta.

D King's Father asked his son to become a Pastor with him in Atlanta.

3 **A** Many people admired King, including President John F. Kennedy.

B Many people admired King, including president John f. Kennedy.

C Many people admired King, including President John f. kennedy.

D Many people admired king, including president John F. kennedy.

4 **A** Both King and his wife, Coretta scott king, worked hard for civil rights.

B Both King and his Wife, Coretta Scott King, worked hard for civil rights.

C Both King and his wife, Coretta Scott King, worked hard for civil rights.

D Both King and his Wife, Coretta scott King, worked hard for civil rights.

Lesson 10
Capitalizing Names of Places and Things

CCSS
L.4.2a: Use correct capitalization.

Introduction You know that a **common noun** names *any* person, place, or thing. A **proper noun** names a *particular* person, place, or thing. Remember to capitalize proper nouns. When a proper noun contains more than one word, begin each important word with a capital letter.

Places	Things
West Park Avenue	Veterans Day
Durham	Pen and Pencil Company, Inc.
Hanging Rock State Park	Green Bay Packers
United States of America	Saturday
Asia	February

Guided Practice Write each sentence correctly. Add capital letters where they are needed.

Hint

When you write the name of a place or thing, do not capitalize small words, such as *a*, *and*, or *of*.

1 We have a big party in our town on the fourth of july.

_____

_____

2 Before the holiday, people put up flags along kinsman drive.

_____

_____

3 This july, the event will begin on monday afternoon.

_____

_____

4 There will be fireworks that night in eagle creek park.

_____

_____

For numbers 1–5, in which sentence are capital letters used correctly?

1 **A** In the United States, Thanksgiving is celebrated in November.

B In the united states, Thanksgiving is celebrated in november.

C In the United States, Thanksgiving is celebrated in november.

D In the united states, thanksgiving is celebrated in November.

2 **A** A similar holiday is celebrated in Canada on the second monday of october.

B A similar holiday is celebrated in Canada on the second Monday of october.

C A similar holiday is celebrated in Canada on the second Monday of October.

D A similar holiday is celebrated in Canada on the second monday of October.

3 **A** In north america, families give thanks as their ancestors from Europe did.

B In North america, families give thanks as their ancestors from europe did.

C In north America, families give thanks as their ancestors from Europe did.

D In North America, families give thanks as their ancestors from Europe did.

4 **A** Last year we went to my aunt's house on scudder st. in Amarillo.

B Last year we went to my aunt's house on Scudder St. in Amarillo.

C Last year we went to my aunt's house on scudder St. in Amarillo.

D Last year we went to my aunt's house on Scudder st. in amarillo.

5 **A** My aunt served pie from Albert And Sons Baking company.

B My aunt served pie from Albert and Sons baking company.

C My aunt served pie from Albert and Sons Baking Company.

D My aunt served pie from Albert and sons Baking Company.

Lesson 11
Punctuating Direct Quotations

👥 **Introduction** Using a **direct quotation**, or a person's exact words, can help make your writing come alive. You can write the exact words of a character in a story, or you can write what someone in real life has said or written. Use **quotation marks** (" ") before and after the exact words of a speaker or author.

- A direct quotation can come at the beginning of a sentence.

> "I can't wait to see the Washington Monument!" said Elena.

- A direct quotation can also come at the end of a sentence. Use a **comma** (,) to separate the beginning of the sentence from the quotation.

> Author Rachel White wrote, "The Washington Monument is one of the most popular tourist attractions in the United States."

- Use quotation marks only when you are showing a person's exact words, not when you are explaining what the person said.

> Nathan said, "I look forward to the trip to Washington."
>
> Nathan said that he looks forward to the trip to Washington.

👥 **Guided Practice** **Add the correct punctuation where it is needed in each sentence.**

Hint

Be sure the end punctuation after a speaker's words is inside the quotation marks.

Example:
Len asked, "Where have you been?"
"I've been right here!" I shouted.

1. I'm almost ready to go! exclaimed Kris.

2. Mr. Mendez said Before we go, we need to learn about the Washington Monument.

3. Why did they build the monument? Alva asked.

4. Kris replied It was built to honor George Washington.

5. The monument is a symbol of his leadership, wrote author Rachel White.

For numbers 1–4, which sentence in each group uses the correct punctuation?

Answer Form

1 Ⓐ Ⓑ Ⓒ Ⓓ
2 Ⓐ Ⓑ Ⓒ Ⓓ
3 Ⓐ Ⓑ Ⓒ Ⓓ   **Number**   /4
4 Ⓐ Ⓑ Ⓒ Ⓓ   **Correct**

1 **A** The Washington Monument is huge!"
Anna exclaimed.

B "The Washington Monument is huge!
Anna exclaimed.

C "The Washington Monument is huge"! Anna exclaimed.

D "The Washington Monument is huge!" Anna exclaimed.

2 **A** The tour guide said, "The monument is more than 555 feet tall."

B The tour guide said "The monument is more than 555 feet tall."

C The tour guide said, The monument is more than 555 feet tall.

D The tour guide, said "The monument is more than 555 feet tall."

3 **A** Author Carter Bailey wrote, More than 500,000 visitors go to the top of the monument in most years."

B Author Carter Bailey wrote, "More than 500,000 visitors go to the top of the monument in most years."

C Author Carter Bailey wrote "More than 500,000 visitors go to the top of the monument in most years."

D Author Carter Bailey wrote More than 500,000 visitors go to the top of the monument in most years.

4 **A** The monument is temporarily closed for repairs, the officer said.

B "The monument is temporarily closed for repairs, the officer said.

C "The monument is temporarily closed for repairs," the officer said.

D The monument is temporarily closed for repairs," the officer said.

Lesson 12
Using Commas with Coordinating Conjunctions

CCSS
L.4.2c: Use a comma before a coordinating conjunction in a compound sentence.

Introduction Sometimes you can make your writing sound less choppy by combining two sentences into a **compound sentence**. A compound sentence is two sentences joined together by the **coordinating conjunction** *and*, *but*, *or*, or *so*. There is usually a comma before the conjunction.

> The United States has many national parks. Yosemite is one of the oldest.
>
> The United States has many national parks, **and** Yosemite is one of the oldest.

> It is home to many animals. It also has unusual plant life.
>
> It is home to many animals, **but** it also has unusual plant life.

> You can camp at Yosemite. You can stay in a hotel.
>
> You can camp at Yosemite, **or** you can stay in a hotel.

> I love seeing wildlife. I want to visit Yosemite.
>
> I love seeing wildlife, **so** I want to visit Yosemite.

Guided Practice Combine each pair of sentences to make a compound sentence. Choose the correct coordinating conjunction in parentheses ( ).

Hint

Use *and* when you mean "also." Use *but* when you want to show a difference. Use *or* when you want to show a choice. Use *so* when you want to give a reason or show a result.

1 You may bring your dog to Yosemite. Dogs are only allowed on paved trails. (or, but) _____

_____

2 There are wild animals in the park. You need to be careful as you hike. (so, but) _____

_____

3 You should never leave food out in the open. You must remove your garbage. (but, and) _____

_____

For numbers 1–4, what is the correct way to write the underlined part of each sentence?

1 Yosemite became a national park in 1890 and today millions of people explore it.

   A in 1890 but today millions

   B in 1890 and, today millions

   C in 1890, and today millions

   D in 1890 so, today millions

2 At Yosemite's museum you can read books so you can look at photographs on the walls.

   A books, or you can look at

   B books, so you can look at

   C books or, you can look at

   D books but, you can look at

3 The park is open all year round but some of the roads close in winter.

   A all year round or some

   B all year round, but some

   C all year round, or some

   D all year round but, some

4 Yosemite is filled with natural wonders, or enjoy it when you visit!

   A natural wonders, but, enjoy

   B natural wonders so enjoy

   C natural wonders, so enjoy

   D natural wonders, and enjoy

Lesson 13
Precise Words and Phrases

CCSS
L.4.3a: Choose words and phrases to convey ideas precisely.

Introduction What is the difference between a dog and a puppy? Maybe 10 years! If you just used the term *dog,* a reader would never know you meant *a brown bulldog puppy*. It is important to choose words and phrases that tell **precisely** the meaning you wish to convey.

- Using precise words helps to convey your ideas exactly as you intended.

Vague: Parts of Hawaii have been disappearing.	**Precise: Wetlands** of Hawaii have been disappearing.

- Using precise phrases will help readers picture and understand what you mean.

Vague: Many fruits grow in Hawaii.	**Precise: Tropical pineapples, mangos, and bananas** grow in Hawaii.

Guided Practice Read each sentence. Circle the word or phrase that conveys a more precise meaning for the vague underlined words. Tell a partner what additional information each phrase adds to the original sentence.

Hint

Ask yourself which word or phrase best helps you to picture or understand what is being described.

1 Hawaii has a lot of the coral reefs in the world.

    a majority   **a large number**

2 Oahu is filled with tourists who want to enjoy the island's beautiful beaches.

    white-sand   **pretty**

3 The North Shore is the ideal location to watch big-wave surfing, as waves go up more than 30 feet high.

    move   **stretch**

4 Hanauma Bay, with its nice waters, is popular for snorkeling.

    clear blue   **pleasant**

5 Tall mountains can be found on the "Big Island" in Hawaii.

    High   **Towering**

For numbers 1–3, read each sentence. Which word or phrase best replaces the underlined text in the sentence?

1 Maui has <u>good</u> rainforests.

  A nice

  B special

  C wide and large

  D lush and fertile

For numbers 4 and 5, read the paragraph and choose the correct answer.

An inactive volcano, Diamond Head, is the most famous <u>place</u> on the island of Oahu. Most volcanoes, like Diamond Head, rarely erupt. But when they do, <u>hot</u> lava can blaze wildly.

2 The <u>big</u> cliffs on the island of Kauai were in the movie *Jurassic Park 3*.

  A full

  B great

  C steep

  D large

4 Choose a word to replace <u>place</u> that better describes what Diamond Head is.

  A area

  B spot

  C section

  D landmark

3 One waterfall on the "Big Island" <u>goes down</u> into a large bowl-shaped gulch.

  A falls

  B jumps

  C moves

  D plunges

5 Choose a word to replace <u>hot</u> that better describes volcanic lava.

  A fiery

  B grand

  C warm

  D heavy

Punctuation for Effect

CCSS
L.4.3b: Choose punctuation for effect.

Introduction You know that a sentence is a group of words that expresses a complete thought. Sentences can end with a period (**.**), a question mark (**?**), or an exclamation point (**!**). Using a variety of sentence types will make your writing more interesting to read.

Sentence Type	Example
Statement	Summer is my favorite time of year.
Question	What season do you like best?
Exclamation	This summer, I went white-water rafting!
Command	Tell me when you get my photos.

- Instead of beginning a report with a statement, try beginning with a question.
  Statement: At the end of the summer, we went kayaking.
  Question: Have you ever tried kayaking on a hot summer day?

- If you want to express strong emotion, consider writing an exclamation instead of a statement.
  Statement: Kayaking is an exciting sport.
  Exclamation: What an exciting sport kayaking is!

Guided Practice Rewrite each sentence as either a question or an exclamation. Tell a partner how the change in punctuation changes the meaning of the sentence.

Hint

Think about how the end punctuation you choose will affect the way the reader "hears" your sentences and understands your meaning.

1 You all must wear lifejackets. (question)

_____

2 Kayaking is easy to learn. (question)

_____

3 There are rocks ahead. (exclamation)

_____

4 I enjoy kayaking. (exclamation)

_____

Read the passage on kayaking. For numbers 1–4, choose the most effective way to rewrite the sentences.

(1) I like nature and adventure. (2) Kayaking is a great way to experience both. (3) We set out on a sunny clear day. (4) It was easy paddling, and we were having a good time. (5) Someone shouted, "Rocks ahead." (6) Then I shouted back. (7) "Can you move to the left of them now?" (8) We were lucky to escape the rocks. (9) Suddenly, I saw lightning and heard a huge clap of thunder. (10) "Oh no, we're going to be struck by lightning."

1 Which rewrite of sentence 1 makes the most engaging opening?

  A You like nature, and you like adventure.

  B Do you like nature and adventure?

  C You should like nature and adventure.

  D What about nature and adventure?

2 Which rewrite of sentence 5 shows strong emotion?

  A Someone shouted, "Rocks Ahead."

  B Someone shouted, "Rocks ahead?"

  C Someone shouted, "Rocks ahead!"

  D Someone shouted that rocks were ahead.

3 Which rewrite of sentence 7 best gives the effect of a command, or orders?

  A "You could now move to the left of them."

  B "Move to the left of them now."

  C "Why not move to the left of them now?"

  D "You would now move to the left of them."

4 What rewrite of sentence 10 best shows strong emotion?

  A "Oh, no. We're going to be struck by lightning?"

  B "Oh, no? We're going to be struck by lightning!"

  C "Oh, no! We're going to be struck by lightning!"

  D "Oh no? We're going to be struck by lightning?"

Lesson 15
Formal and Informal Language

CCSS
L.4.3c: Differentiate between contexts that call for formal English (e.g., presenting ideas) and situations where informal discourse is appropriate (e.g., small-group discussion).

Introduction You probably don't think much about the words you use or the way you speak when talking with friends. You probably take shortcuts, using contractions, one-word answers, and incomplete sentences. You might even use slang expressions, such as *hey*, *cool*, and *awesome*.

- **Informal language** is the language you use with friends in small-group discussions or in casual situations.

> *Three friends talking on the playground:*
> **Ben:** Hey, how was the field trip?
> **Sachi:** Pretty neat, dude. Like the museum's got all this totally cool old stuff.

- **Formal language** is the language you use in school or in other important situations. When you use formal language, you use words correctly and speak in complete sentences.

> *From Jacob's report about the class field trip:*
> On Monday, we visited the North Carolina Museum of History. We were able to visit many interesting exhibits about the history of our state.

Guided Practice Read each sentence. Label the sentence either *F* for *formal* or *I* for *informal*. Then talk with a partner about a situation or setting in which the language might be appropriate.

Hint

More serious occasions and fancy settings require formal language. Formal language is also used to show respect for others, such as teachers or bosses.

1. At the museum, we saw a full-size model of the *1903 Wright Flyer.* _____

2. Man, I can't believe the model wasn't the real thing. _____

3. The first successful flight took place in Kitty Hawk, North Carolina. _____

4. What a short flight! Just twelve seconds, but so awesome. _____

5. Orville and Wilbur Wright had invented the first airplane, and now people could fly. _____

For numbers 1 and 2, in which situation or setting would you use formal language?

1 **A** at a family cookout

   B speaking in front of the class

   C making plans with friends

   D at summer camp

2 **A** at the beach

   B at a soccer game

   C speaking to a mayor or other official

   D talking about a movie with a friend

For number 3, which sentence is the most formal request?

3 **A** Can I go see the coolest movie ever with my friends?

   B It would be super cool for me to see a movie with my friends, okay?

   C May I please go to see a movie with my friends?

   D Let me go to a movie with my friends, please?

Answer Form

1 Ⓐ Ⓑ Ⓒ Ⓓ
2 Ⓐ Ⓑ Ⓒ Ⓓ
3 Ⓐ Ⓑ Ⓒ Ⓓ
4 Ⓐ Ⓑ Ⓒ Ⓓ   **Number** ╱5
5 Ⓐ Ⓑ Ⓒ Ⓓ   **Correct**

For numbers 4 and 5, in which situation or setting would you use informal language?

4 **A** sharing a project at a science fair

   B sharing great news with your family

   C presenting a report in your class

   D asking a librarian to help find a book

5 **A** at an event honoring your aunt or uncle

   B asking a police officer for directions

   C speaking with the school principal

   D at baseball practice with your friends

Using Context Clues

CCSS
L.4.4a: Use context (e.g., definitions, examples, or restatements in text) as a clue to the meaning of a word or phrase.

👥 Introduction Sometimes when you're reading a story or an article, you'll come across a word you don't know. When you don't know the meaning of a word, often you can figure it out by looking at the words and sentences around it. When you do this, you are using **context clues**.

Kinds of Context Clues	Examples
Look for a **definition** in the text.	In high school, Jim Lovell built his first rocket, a jet engine that could fly to great heights.
Find an **example** that will give you clues about the word's meaning.	Lovell's first attempt was a failure. His rocket flew into the air but then exploded and crashed.
Look for a **restatement**. A restatement happens when the word is discussed in a way that makes its meaning clear.	A rocket is pushed upward by materials that are combustible. These materials burn and release gases.

👥 Guided Practice **Read the paragraph below with a partner. Circle the context clues that help you understand the meaning of the underlined word. Then write down the meanings of the underlined words on the space provided.**

Hint

Sometimes context clues can be found in a sentence before or after the word you're trying to figure out.

Jim Lovell had always been <u>fascinated</u> by rockets. He was interested in learning everything about them and even built his own rocket. Lovell applied to the United States Naval Academy but was <u>rejected</u>. After failing to get into the Academy, Lovell did not give up. He <u>persisted</u>, or kept trying, and finally succeeded. After the Academy, he joined the NASA space program.

fascinated: _____

rejected: _____

persisted: _____

For numbers 1–4, use context clues to figure out the meaning of each underlined word.

NASA chose Lovell to command the *Apollo 13* space mission. Lovell was in charge of two men and of making all final decisions. After they were in space for a little more than two days, Lovell and his crew ran into trouble. One of the oxygen tanks blew up. The explosion caused a leak in another tank, and now there wouldn't be enough oxygen for a moon landing. Lovell and his crew had to return to Earth. Their safe return was due to Lovell's capable leadership.

1 What does the word command mean?

A to study

B to fly with others on

C to be at the head of

D to be part of

2 What words help you understand the meaning of command?

A "in charge of"

B "two men"

C "space mission"

D "chose Lovell"

3 What does the word explosion mean?

A a leak

B a bursting of something

C a lack of oxygen

D leaving outer space

4 What does the word capable suggest about Lovell as a leader?

A He is a gentle and patient leader.

B He is skillful at leading others.

C He is harsh to those he leads.

D He is weak when leading others.

Lesson 17
Greek and Latin Word Parts

CCSS

L.4.4.b: Use common, grade-appropriate Greek and Latin affixes and roots as clues to the meaning of a word (e.g., *telegraph*, *photograph*, *autograph*).

Introduction English words come from many languages, including Greek and Latin.

- A **root** is a word part that usually can't stand alone as a word. Sometimes one root is added to another root to make a word, as in the word *photograph*.

Root	Meaning	Root	Meaning
graph	"write"	*act*	"do"
vis, vid	"see"	*photo*	"light"
phon, phono	"sound, voice"	*port*	"carry"

- **Affixes** are word parts, such as prefixes and suffixes, that are added to word roots to make words. You can add the root *vis* to *-ible* to make *visible*.

Prefix	Meaning	Suffix	Meaning
auto-	"self"	*-ist, -er, -or*	"someone who"
tele-	"distance"	*-able, -ible*	"able or capable"

- As you learn Greek and Latin roots and affixes, your vocabulary will grow.

Guided Practice Circle the roots in the underlined words. Write the meaning of each root. Then tell a partner the meaning of each underlined word.

Hint

Remember, words may have two roots or a root and an affix.

1 My favorite <u>actor</u> is Jesse B.

_____

2 I have five <u>photographs</u> of Jesse B. on my wall.

_____

3 One even has an <u>autograph</u> on it.

_____

4 I've asked my mom if I could <u>telephone</u> Jesse B.

_____

5 She said I could just watch Jesse B. on <u>television</u>.

_____

For numbers 1–4, read each sentence. Then answer the question.

1 I decided to compose a letter to Jesse B.

The prefix *com-* means "with," and the root *poser* means "to put or set down." What is the meaning of <u>compose</u> as used in the sentence?

A to think

B to write

C to talk

D to mail

2 Dear Jesse B., I just read a biography about you.

The prefix *bio-* means "life," and the root *graph* means "write." What is the meaning of <u>biography</u> as used in the sentence?

A writing about the life of an actor

B writing about someone else's life

C writing about the beauty of life

D writing about how to live your life

3 Your life story inspires me and many other fans.

The prefix *in-* can mean "within," and the root *spir* means "breathe." What is the meaning of <u>inspires</u> as used in the sentence?

A causes people to become alive

B causes a heavy wind to blow

C causes people to faint

D causes strong lungs

4 I hear you are a very benevolent person, giving to many charities.

The prefix *bene-* means "well," and the root *velle* means "wish." What is the meaning of <u>benevolent</u> as used in the sentence?

A surrounded by good people

B showing good will to others

C liked by many good people

D hoping others are good

Lesson 18
Using a Dictionary or Glossary

CCSS

L.4.4.c: Consult reference materials (e.g., dictionaries, glossaries . . .), both print and digital, to find the pronunciation and determine or clarify the precise meaning of key words and phrases.

Introduction There are many places you can look to find information about words. A dictionary and a glossary are two kinds of references you can use.

- A **dictionary** lists words in alphabetical order. Each entry has an entry word, the pronunciation, the part of speech, and the meanings of the word.

> **break** (brāk) *v.* **1.** to smash **2.** to disobey **3.** to do better than: *Ina broke the record for the high jump.* *n.* **4.** time off **5.** luck   **break into** **1.** to disturb **2.** to start to do suddenly **3.** to start a new job: *He broke into acting.*

The pronunciation uses special symbols to show how to say the word.

The part of speech is abbreviated. Here it is *v.* for verb.

When there is more than one meaning, each definition is numbered.

Sometimes a sample sentence helps make the meaning of a word or phrase clearer.

- A **glossary** is a kind of dictionary often found at the back of a book. It lists important words from the book in alphabetical order. It gives the meaning of each word as it is used in that book.

> **carry** (kăr´ē) **1.** to move **2.** to hold   **carry on** **1.** to continue **2.** to act excitedly

Guided Practice Read the paragraph. Use the entries above to find the meanings of the underlined words and phrases. Write the number of the correct meaning above each word or phrase.

Hint

To find the right meaning of a word or phrase, read all the definitions first. Decide which meaning makes the most sense in the sentence.

Hank Aaron broke into major league baseball in the 1950s.

A big break came for him in 1954 when he replaced an injured

player. Aaron's talent helped him break Babe Ruth's record of

714 homeruns. When Aaron hit his 715th homerun, his fans

broke into cheers. Aaron carried on hitting homeruns until he

retired in 1976.

Use the dictionary entries to answer numbers 1–4.

---

material (mə tîr´ ē əl) *n.* **1.** fabric or cloth **2.** ideas and facts used in writing something *adj.* **3.** made of matter **4.** having great meaning or effect

---

1 Which definition matches how material is used in this sentence?

Hank Aaron had few material goods growing up, but his parents gave him love and encouragement.

A Definition 1

B Definition 2

C Definition 3

D Definition 4

---

hammer (hăm´ ər) *n.* **1.** a tool used for pounding objects, such as nails **2.** a part of a piano *v.* **3.** to hit hard **4.** to join with nails

---

2 Which definition matches how hammer is used in this sentence?

His skill at hammering baseballs helped Aaron become a successful baseball player.

A Definition 1

B Definition 2

C Definition 3

D Definition 4

---

stand (stănd) *n.* **1.** a display area **2.** an opinion or a position on an issue *v.* **3.** to be on one's feet **4.** to endure, put up with   **stand for 1.** to represent, be a symbol of **2.** to allow **3.** to believe in and support: *He stands for equality.* **4.** an abbreviation for

---

3 Which definition matches how stand is used in this sentence?

Aaron could stand a lot of pressure, too.

A Definition 1

B Definition 2

C Definition 3

D Definition 4

---

4 Which definition matches how stand for is used in this sentence?

Hank Aaron stands for the talent, hard work, and courage that make an athlete great.

A Definition 1

B Definition 2

C Definition 3

D Definition 4

Lesson 19
Similes and Metaphors

CCSS
L.4.5.a: Explain the meaning of simple similes and metaphors (e.g., *as pretty as a picture*) in context.

Introduction Authors sometimes help readers imagine what one thing is like by comparing it to something else. Comparisons can help readers picture what is being described by showing how two things are alike in some way.

- A **simile** makes a comparison using the word *like* or *as*. Look at these similes. The dog's paws are compared to dinner plates. His bark is compared to thunder.

Simile	What It Means
Alicia's dog, Ollie, has *paws* as big as *dinner plates*.	Ollie has very big paws.
His *bark* sounds like *thunder*.	Ollie has a loud bark.

- A **metaphor** makes a comparison without using the word *like* or *as*. In this metaphor, the dog's size is compared to a mountain.

Metaphor	What It Means
Ollie is a *mountain* of a dog.	Ollie is a very large dog.

Guided Practice Find the simile or metaphor in each sentence. Underline the two things being compared. Then write the meaning of the simile or metaphor.

Hint

After you find the two things being compared, ask yourself, *How are they the same?* Use your answer to figure out what each simile or metaphor means.

1 Ollie's mouth was a trap that held a giant stick.

Ollie had a big mouth

2 Ollie leapt toward Alicia like a clumsy ballerina.

He took a big leap

3 Ollie raced past Alicia like a strong wind.

He was running super fast

4 Suddenly, Ollie was a freight train racing into the house.

He going fast into his room

He

For numbers 1–5, read each sentence. Then choose the correct meaning of the underlined simile or metaphor.

1 The stick in Ollie's mouth <u>was a sword</u>, knocking over one object after another.

   A The stick was heavy.

   B The stick was dangerous.

   C Ollie was dangerous.

   D The stick was made of metal.

2 The plates on the table <u>became flying saucers</u> that Alicia had to dodge.

   A Flying saucers came from outer space.

   B Alicia had to play dodge ball.

   C Alicia had to fly across the kitchen.

   D Plates flew through the air.

3 Salad covered the floor <u>like a large blanket.</u>

   A The salad was warm.

   B The salad tasted awful.

   C There was a large blanket on the floor.

   D A layer of salad covered the floor.

4 The floor was <u>as sticky as glue</u>.

   A Glue covered the floor.

   B The floor was a glue stick.

   C The floor was very sticky.

   D Glue made the floor sticky.

5 Alicia <u>was a whirlwind</u> as she cleaned up the mess.

   A Alicia spun wildly.

   B Alicia worked quickly.

   C Alicia was getting tired.

   D Alicia was breathing hard.

Lesson 20
Idioms

CCSS
L.4.5.b: Recognize and explain the meaning of common idioms. . . .

Introduction Have you ever been "in hot water"? When you hear these words, you might think about taking a hot bath. Or you might think about being in trouble. Phrases in English sometimes have more than one meaning.

- An **idiom** is an expression whose meaning is different from the meaning of its individual words. The idiom *up to my ears* means "very busy with."

> I was up to my ears in homework when my friend Mai called.

- The phrase *up to my ears* has a **literal** meaning, too. The meaning of the phrase is the same as the meaning of the individual words.

> I was chilly, so I pulled my sweater up to my ears.

Guided Practice Read each sentence. Underline the idiom. Then circle the correct meaning of the idiom.

Hint

If an idiom doesn't make sense, use context clues to help you understand it. Sometimes you can also find the meaning of idioms in a dictionary.

1. I knew Mai would talk my ear off if she had the chance.

   talk until my ear fell off   (**talk a long time**)   **talk loudly**

2. So I said, "My mom will fly off the handle if I'm on the phone and not studying."

   throw a pot   (**get angry**)   **take a trip**

3. I explained, "I'm in the doghouse because I didn't do well on my last spelling test."

   (**in trouble**)   **sitting in a doghouse**   **playing with the dog**

4. Mai said, "I don't want to rock the boat, so come over later."

   go boating   **throw rocks**   (**cause problems**)

5. It rained cats and dogs as I biked to Mai's house.

   was dark   **was foggy**   (**rained heavily**)

6. I knew I had to make tracks, or I'd soon be completely wet.

   slow down   (**hurry**)   **take a train**

For numbers 1–5, read each sentence. Then choose the correct meaning of each underlined idiom.

1 I was <u>all ears</u> when Mai shared her news.

   A feeling my ears grow

   B getting a headache

   Ⓒ listening carefully

   D unable to hear

2 Mai said, "I've just heard it <u>from the horse's mouth</u>. Our school is going to have an auction to raise money."

   A from a horse trainer

   B from an animal doctor

   C from the mouth of a horse

   Ⓓ from a trustworthy person

3 I <u>held my tongue</u> even though I knew that Mai probably found out from her mom, our school principal.

   Ⓐ kept quiet

   B grabbed my tongue

   C stuck out my tongue

   D made a funny face

4 Mai continued, "Let's <u>put our heads together</u> and think of something to contribute to the auction."

   A whisper quietly

   B sit next to one another

   Ⓒ work together to make a plan

   D put our heads on the table

5 Mai is <u>head and shoulders above me</u> at cooking. I suggested that she bake a cake to sell at the auction.

   A much taller than I am

   Ⓑ much better than I am

   C standing above me

   D faster than I am

Lesson 21
Adages and Proverbs

CCSS
L.4.5.b: Recognize and explain the meaning of common . . . adages, and proverbs.

Introduction Like idioms, **adages** and **proverbs** are also expressions that you cannot understand just by knowing the meanings of the individual words. Learning the meanings of these expressions can help you better understand what an author has written.

- An **adage** is a well-known saying that people have come to believe because it has been used for a long time.

Adage	Meaning
Variety is the spice of life.	Trying different things makes life interesting.

- A **proverb** is also an old, well-known saying. It sometimes gives advice about how to behave.

Proverb	Meaning
Look before you leap.	Think carefully about what you are going to do before you do it.

Guided Practice Read the paragraph. Number and underline each adage and proverb. Then write the meaning of each on the lines provided.

Hint

If the meaning of a saying isn't clear, use context clues to help you understand what the words mean. You can also search online to find the meanings of many adages and proverbs.

My friend Omar is a great runner. He doesn't look like an athlete, but I never judge a book by its cover. Last week, we went running together. I thought I'd be able to keep up with him, but I couldn't. I told myself to keep going because there's no gain without pain. When I thought I would faint, I stopped to rest. After all, it's better to be safe than sorry.

cover.

1 I never judge a book by it

2 No gain without pain.

3 It's better to be safe than sorry

For numbers 1–4, read each sentence. Then choose the correct meaning of each underlined adage or proverb.

1 Omar said, "Remember, <u>slow and steady wins the race.</u> Run a little each day, and soon you'll become a good runner."

A If you run slowly, you will win races.

B It is better to run slowly than to win a race.

C Slow workers have the most success.

D Patience and hard work bring success.

2 I promised to run every day, but that was <u>easier said than done.</u>

A easily said

B easily done

C easier to talk about than to do

D easier to run than to promise

3 Then I thought, "If I want to be a good runner, I have to practice. I know that <u>practice makes perfect!</u>"

A Being perfect is important.

B You must practice perfectly.

C You must practice something every day.

D Practicing is the way to get good at something.

4 When I won my first race, <u>I gave credit where credit was due,</u> and I thanked Omar for helping me.

A used a credit card to pay a bill

B gave thanks to someone who deserved it

C gave money that was owed to someone

D had to give away the prize

Lesson 22
Synonyms and Antonyms

CCSS

L.4.5.c: Demonstrate understanding of words by relating them to their opposites (antonyms) and to words with similar but not identical meanings (synonyms).

Introduction Words in English can have meanings that are similar or different. If you know how two words are related, you can sometimes use the meaning of a word you already know to understand the meaning of an unfamiliar word.

- A **synonym** is a word that has the same or almost the same meaning as another word. The words *select* and *choose* are synonyms.

> I try to **select** foods from all five food groups.
>
> I often seem to **choose** the same foods, though.

- An **antonym** is a word that has the opposite meaning of another word. The words *forget* and *remember* are antonyms.

> Sometimes I **forget** to eat different kinds of vegetables.
>
> I need to **remember** to vary my diet.

- If you find yourself using the same word again and again, replace the repeated word with a synonym. This will make your writing more interesting.

Guided Practice Read each sentence. Write *S* next to the synonym for the underlined word. Write *A* next to the antonym.

Hint

You can use a thesaurus to find synonyms and antonyms for many words. Sometimes a dictionary also lists synonyms and antonyms.

1 I made a <u>large</u> salad with many vegetables.

    enormous _____   **tiny** _____

2 A salad is a meal that is <u>easy</u> to make.

    challenging _____   **simple** _____

3 I used vegetables that are <u>commonly</u> grown in our area.

    unusually _____   **normally** _____

4 I bought them at our <u>local</u> farmer's market.

    distant _____   **nearby** _____

For numbers 1–3, which word is a synonym for the underlined word as it is used in each sentence?

1 My doctor <u>asked</u> me about my diet.

   A answered

   B questioned

   C told

   D informed

2 She said that healthy food can also be <u>tasty</u>.

   A sweet

   B sour

   C enjoyable

   D delicious

3 She gave me a few <u>interesting</u> recipes.

   A dull

   B exciting

   C boring

   D tiring

Answer Form

1 Ⓐ Ⓑ Ⓒ Ⓓ
2 Ⓐ Ⓑ Ⓒ Ⓓ
3 Ⓐ Ⓑ Ⓒ Ⓓ
4 Ⓐ Ⓑ Ⓒ Ⓓ   **Number**
5 Ⓐ Ⓑ Ⓒ Ⓓ   **Correct** /5

For numbers 4 and 5, which word is an antonym for the underlined word as it is used in each sentence?

4 Is it <u>important</u> to eat foods that have protein?

   A unnecessary

   B required

   C needed

   D helpful

5 Can you <u>get</u> protein from meat, eggs, and fish?

   A gather

   B gain

   C lose

   D collect

Lesson 23
Using a Thesaurus

CCSS
L.4.4.c: Consult reference materials (e.g., ... thesauruses), both print and digital, to ... determine or clarify the precise meaning of key words ....

Introduction A thesaurus, like a dictionary, is another kind of reference you can use to learn about words.

• A **thesaurus** lists words in alphabetical order. Each entry has an entry word, the part of speech, the word's meaning, and synonyms. Sometimes antonyms are listed at the end of the entry.

> **conceal** *v.* to hide someone or something: *Bushes conceal the entrance to the cave.* **camouflage, hide, shield** *Antonyms: reveal, uncover*

> **principal** *adj.* **1.** the main, or most important: *Drawing is my principal hobby.* **major, main, chief, prime** *Antonyms: lesser, minor* **n. 2.** someone who is the head of a school: *The principal enforces our school rules.* **head, chief, leader**

> A sample sentence helps make a word's meaning clearer.

> Synonyms for the word follow the sample sentence.

> When there is more than one meaning, each definition is numbered and includes the abbreviated part of speech.

• You can use a thesaurus to find precise words or to replace vague words. Learning synonyms for an unfamiliar word can also help you understand the word's meaning.

Guided Practice Read the paragraph. Use the thesaurus entries above to answer the questions about the underlined words.

Hint

Remember, synonyms are words that have the same or almost the same meaning. Antonyms have opposite meanings.

Cougars are powerful hunters. They often <u>conceal</u> themselves among rocks or in trees before attacking their prey. Deer are their <u>principal</u> prey, but cougars hunt other animals, too.

1 Which words are synonyms for the word *conceal* as used in the paragraph? _____

_____

2 Which definition number helps you understand the meaning of the word *principal* as it is used in the paragraph? _____

3 Which words are antonyms for the word *principal* as it is used in the paragraph? _____

For numbers 1–4, read the sentence. Then use the thesaurus entry to answer the question.

---

uncertain *adj.* doubtful: *I'm uncertain if it will rain tomorrow.* **unsure, unclear, doubtful, unpredictable** *Antonyms: certain, predictable, sure*

---

1 The future of cougars is uncertain.

Which is a synonym for <u>uncertain</u> as it is used above?

A sure

B certain

C clear

D unclear

---

defend *v.* to keep safe from harm: *Dogs defend their puppies.* **protect, guard, shield** *Antonyms: attack, assault*

---

2 Ranchers defend their livestock against cougars.

Which is an antonym for <u>defend</u> as it is used above?

A guard

B protect

C attack

D shield

---

decrease *v.* **1.** to become smaller: *The size of the ice cube decreased as it melted.* **lessen, reduce, shrink** *Antonyms: increase, grow, rise*   *n.* **2.** the process of getting smaller **drop, decline, shrinking, reduction** *Antonyms: increase, growth*

---

3 Cougar populations decrease partly because of hunting.

Which is a synonym for <u>decrease</u> as it is used above?

A rise

B shrink

C grow

D increase

---

4 Destroying areas where cougars live also decreases the population.

Which is an antonym for <u>decreases</u> as it is used above?

A grows

B shrinks

C drops

D lessens

Lesson 24
Precise Words for Actions and Feelings

CCSS

L.4.6: Acquire and use accurately grade appropriate . . . words and phrases, including those that signal precise actions, emotions, or states of being (e.g., *quizzed*, *whined*, *stammered*). . . .

Introduction **Vague** words, like *went*, *mad*, and *nice*, do not often paint a picture in a reader's mind. **Precise** words, like *stumbled*, *fuming*, and *gentle*, give more information. Often, you can use a thesaurus to find the precise word you need.

- Use precise action words and phrases to tell exactly what is happening.

Vague	Precise		
ask	inquire	question	quiz
cry	whine	weep	wail
stop	halt	pause	wrap up

- Use precise words and phrases to describe emotions and states of being.

Vague	Precise		
happy	content	thrilled	tickled pink
sad	grim	woeful	suffering
shy	afraid	modest	bashful

Guided Practice **Read each sentence. Circle the precise word or phrase that best replaces the underlined text.**

Hint

Ask yourself which word or phrase creates the strongest image in your mind. Also, look for clues in the surrounding words to help you decide which words to choose.

1. Female sea turtles <u>go</u> ashore at night to lay eggs on sandy beaches.

   walk   move   crawl

2. <u>Confused</u> sea turtles will not lay eggs on brightly lit beaches.

   Shy   Bewildered   Mysterious

3. <u>Kind</u> people turn off their outdoor lights.

   Gentle   Good   Caring

4. After laying eggs, a sea turtle <u>goes away from</u> her nest of eggs and returns to the sea.

   rejects   quits on   deserts

5. Volunteers have to <u>put up</u> fences to protect nest sites.

   prepare   construct   form

For numbers 1–5, read each sentence. Then choose the most precise word or phrase that best replaces the underlined text in the sentence.

1 Many people <u>see</u> sea turtles hatching from their nests.

  A spy

  B observe

  C note

  D eye

2 Volunteers protect the hatchlings by keeping overly <u>excited</u> visitors away from the hatchlings.

  A content

  B eager

  C pleased

  D cheerful

3 Newly hatched sea turtles <u>go quickly</u> to the sea.

  A scamper

  B take off

  C make their way

  D move on out

4 Many predators, such as crabs, <u>eat</u> hatchlings.

  A prey on

  B have

  C nibble

  D snack on

5 Pollution <u>causes problems for</u> sea turtles, too.

  A pains

  B questions

  C upsets

  D endangers